The Great Songs of The Sixties.

Wise Publications
London/New York/Sydney/Cologne

Exclusive Distributors:
Music Sales Limited
78 Newman Street, London WIP 3LA, England
Music Sales Pty. Limited
27 Clarendon Street, Artarmon, Sydney, NSW 2064, Australia

This book © Copyright 1973 and 1985 by
Wise Publications
ISBN 0.7119.0800.1
Order No. AM 61623

Cover and book designed by Pearce Marchbank.
Cover photography by Gered Mankowitz
Styling by Joy Holmes.

Music Sales complete catalogue lists thousands of
titles and is free from your local music book shop,
or direct from Music Sales Limited.
Please send 25p in stamps for postage to
Music Sales Limited, 78 Newman Street, London WIP 3LA.

Printed and bound in Hungary at Kossuth Press
Contractors: I.P.V. Vue Touristique Publishing House Budapest

All My Loving.

Words and music by John Lennon and Paul McCartney.

Brightly

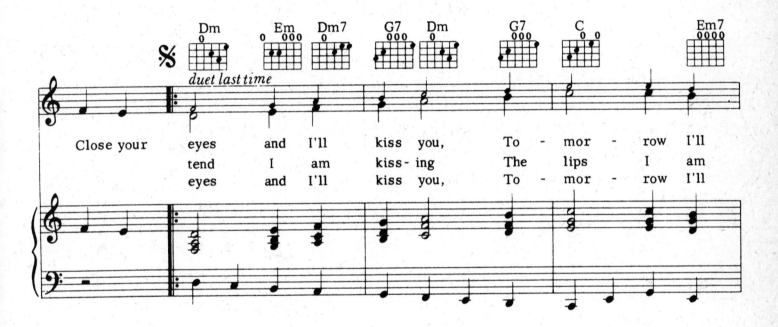

duet last time

Close your eyes and I'll kiss you, To - mor - row I'll
tend I am kiss - ing The lips I am
eyes and I'll kiss you, To - mor - row I'll

miss you, Re - mem - ber I'll al - ways_ be true. _____
miss - ing, And hope that my dreams will _ come true. _____
miss you, Re - mem - ber I'll al - ways_ be true. _____

And then while I'm a-way___ I'll write home ev-'ry day,___

___ And I'll send all my lov-ing ___ to you.___

2 I'll pre - ___ All my lov-ing ___

I will send to you, _____ All my

lov-ing,__ dar - ling, I'll be true._____ 3 Close your

D.S. al ⊕ 𝄋

⊕ *Coda*

__ All my lov-ing __ I will send to you. _____

7

Anyone Who Had A Heart.

Words by Hal David.
Music by Burt F. Bacharach.

Very slowly

An-y-one who e-ver loved____ could look at me _____ and know that I love   you.

An-y-one who e-ver dreamed__ could look at me_____ and know I dream of   you,

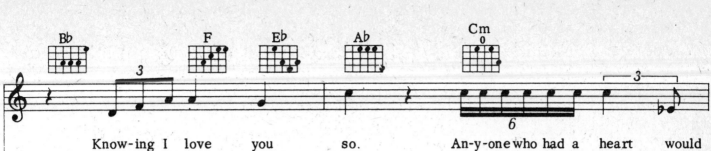

Know-ing I love you so. An-y-one who had a heart would

take me____ in his arms and____ love me

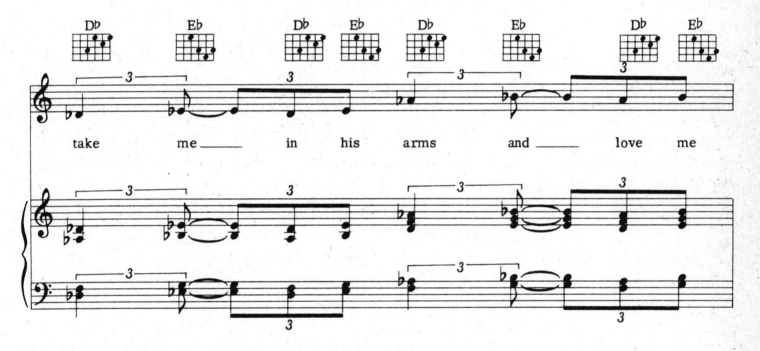

too, You could-n't real-ly have a heart and

hurt me like you hurt me, and be so un-

true. What am I to do?___

Ev-'ry time you go a-way___ I al-ways say,___

___ This time it's good-bye, dear. Lov-ing you the way I do,___ I take you back;___

With-out you I'd die, dear. Know-ing I love you

so. An - y - one who had a heart would

take me ___ in his arms and ___ love me

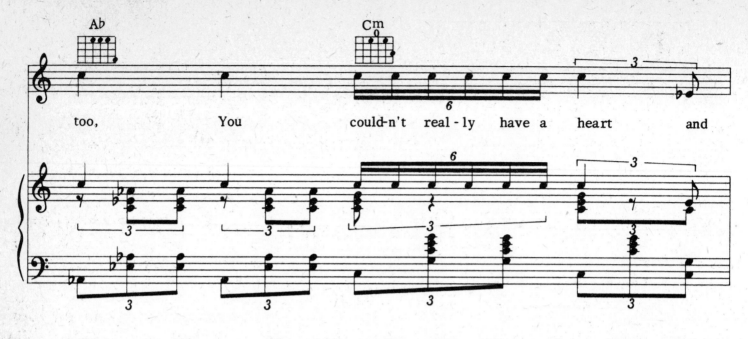

too, You could-n't real-ly have a heart and

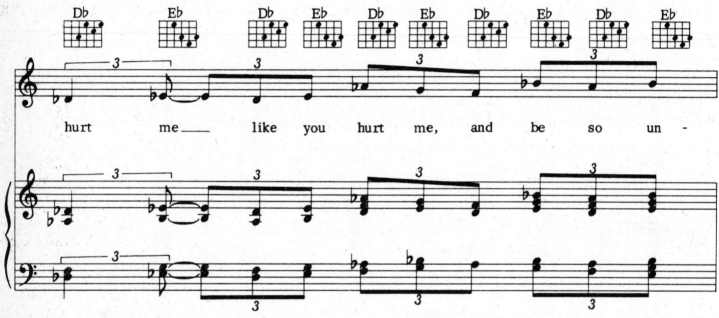

hurt me ___ like you hurt me, and be so un -

true. What am I to do? ___

true._____ An - y - one who had a heart would love me

too._____ An - y - one who had a heart would sure-ly

take me____ in his arms and ____ al - ways

love me, Why won't you?____

Aquarius.

Words by James Rado and Gerome Ragni.
Music by Galt MacDermot.

When the moon _____ is in the sev-enth house, _____

_____ and Ju - pi - ter _____ a - ligns with

Mars, _____ Then peace _____ will guide_ the_

plan - ets, _____ And love will steer the

Tacet
stars; This is the dawn - ing of the age of A - quar - i - us, The

age of A - quar - i - us. _____ A -

quar - i - us,_____ A-

Fine

quar - i - us._____

Har-mo-ny and un-der - stand - - ing, Sym-pa-thy and trust a - bound-

- ing._____ No more false-hoods or de - ri - - sions, Gold - en

Answer Me.

by Gerhard Winkler and Fred Rauch.
English lyric by Carl Sigman.

Moderate waltz

An-swer me, oh my love, Just what sin have I been guil-ty of?

Tell me how I came to lose your love. Please an-swer me, my love.

You were mine yes-ter-day, I be-lieved that love was here to stay,

Won't you tell me where I've gone a-stray? Please an-swer me, my love.

If you're hap-pi-er with-out me, I'll try not to care,

But if you still think a - bout me, Please lis-ten to my prayer.

You must know   I've been true,   Won't you say that we can   start a - new.

In my sor-row now I   turn to you, Please an-swer me, my love.   love.

The Ballad Of Bonnie And Clyde.

Words and music by Mitch Murray and Peter Callander.

Moderato

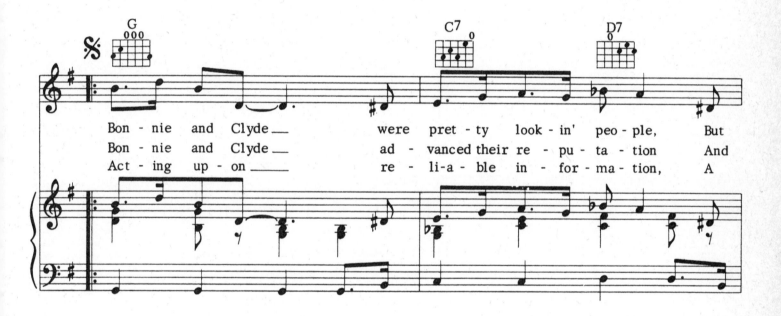

Bon - nie and Clyde ___ were pret - ty look - in' peo - ple, But
Bon - nie and Clyde ___ ad - vanced their re - pu - ta - tion And
Act - ing up - on ___ re - li - a - ble in - for - ma - tion, A

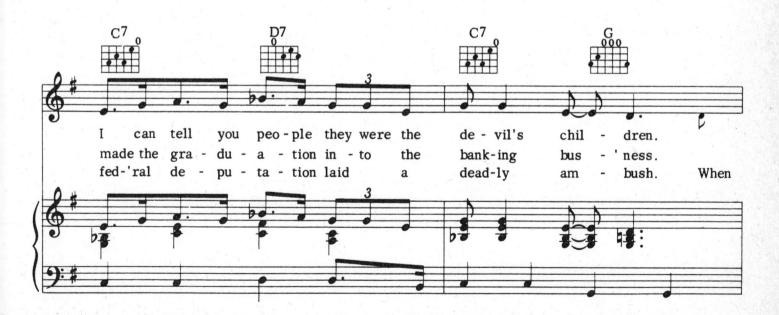

I can tell you peo - ple they were the de - vil's chil - dren.
made the gra - du - a - tion in - to the bank - ing bus - 'ness.
fed-'ral de - pu - ta - tion laid a dead - ly am - bush. When

Bon - nie and Clyde ___ be - gan their e - vil do - in'   One
"Reach for the sky!" ___ sweet - talk - ing Clyde would hol - ler   As
Bon - nie and Clyde ___ came walk - ing in the sun - shine   A

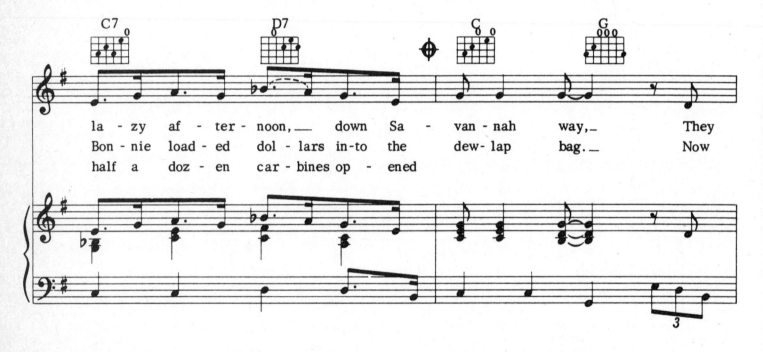

la - zy af - ter - noon, ___ down Sa - van - nah   way, ___   They
Bon - nie load - ed dol - lars in - to the dew - lap   bag. ___   Now
half a doz - en car - bines op - ened

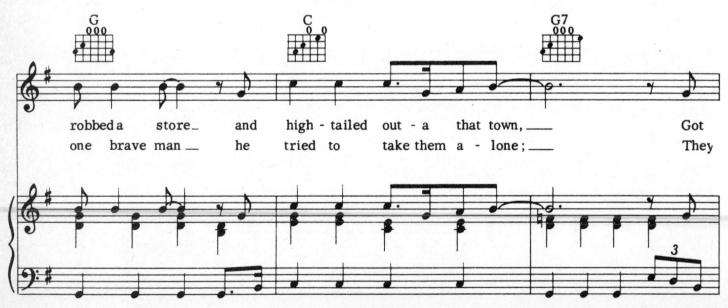

robbed a store ___ and high - tailed out - a that town, ___   Got
one brave man ___ he tried to take them a - lone; ___   They

clean a - way____ in a sto-len car____ and wait - ed till the heat died____
left him ly- ing in a pool of blood____ and laughed a - bout it all the way

down.
home.

Bon - nie and Clyde got to be pub - lic e - ne - my num - ber one,____

23

morn-ing dew._

D.S. al ⊕ 𝄉

Coda

slowly

up on them._ *(gun fight effects)* Bon-nie and Clyde,_ they lived a lot to-ge-ther And

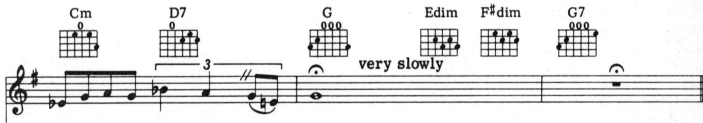

very slowly

fin-al-ly to - ge - ther they_ died.

Blowin' In The Wind.

Words and music by Bob Dylan.

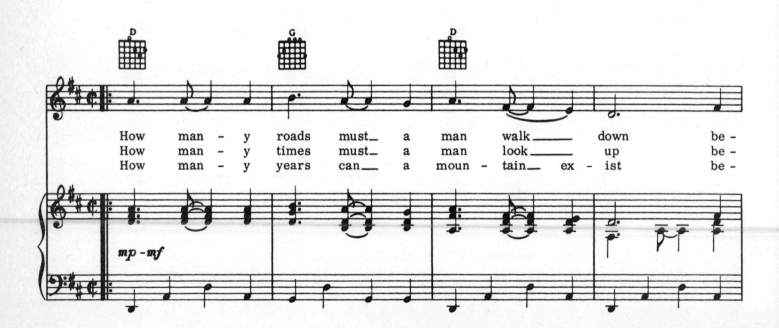

How man - y roads must_ a man walk_____ down be -
How man - y times must_ a man look_____ up be -
How man - y years can_ a moun - tain ex - ist be -

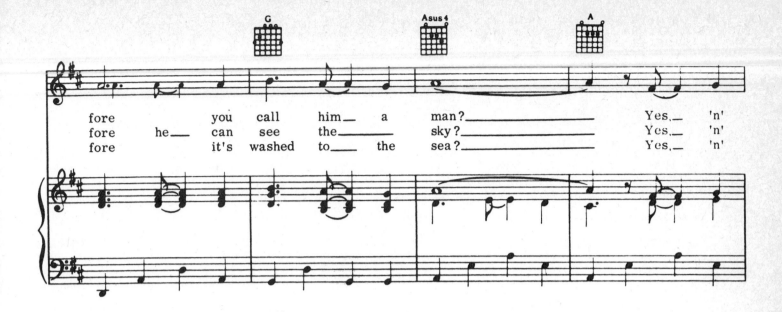

fore   you   call   him   a   man?_____ Yes,__ 'n'
fore   he__ can   see   the_____ sky?_____ Yes,__ 'n'
fore   it's   washed   to___ the   sea?_____ Yes,__ 'n'

how   man - y   seas   must__ a   white   dove_____
how   man - y   ears   must__ one   man_____
how   man - y   years   can__ some   peo - ple__ ex -

sail   be - fore   she   sleeps   in___ the
have   be - fore   he__ can   hear   peo - ple
ist   be - fore   they're__ al - lowed   to___ be

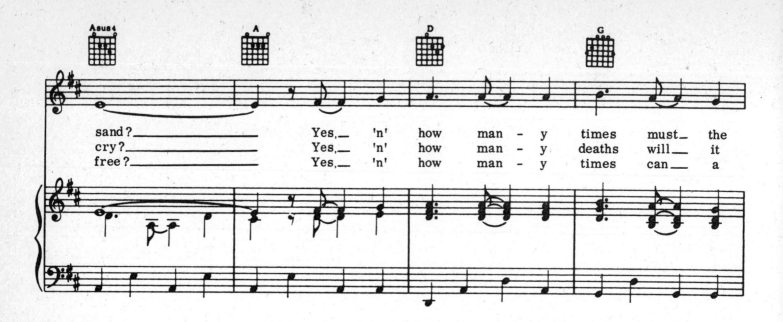

sand?_____ Yes, __ 'n' how man - y times must__ the
cry?_____ Yes,__ 'n' how man - y deaths will__ it
free?_____ Yes,__ 'n' how man - y times can__ a

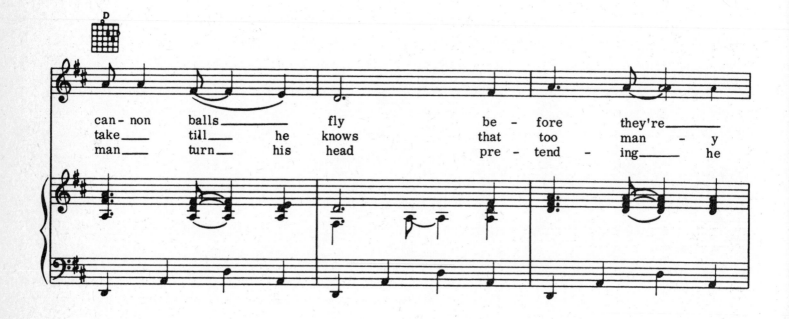

can - non balls_____ fly be - fore they're_____
take__ till__ he flies knows that too man - y
man__ turn__ his head pre - tend - ing_____ he

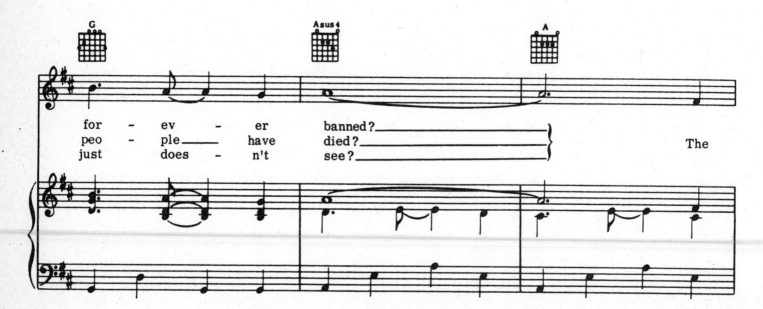

for - ev - er banned?_____
peo - ple____ er have died?_____ The
just does - n't see?_____

28

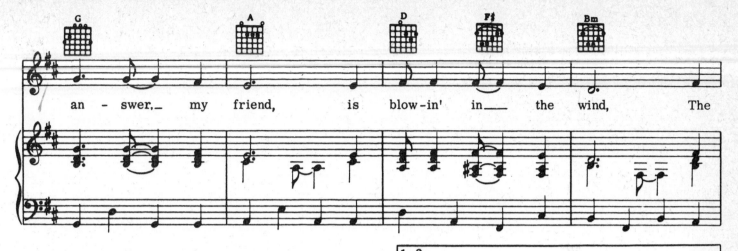

an - swer,_ my friend, is blow-in' in_ the wind, The

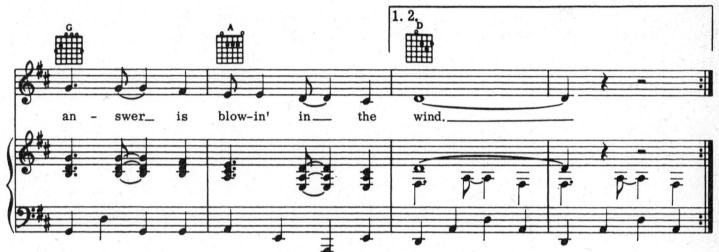

an - swer_ is blow-in' in_ the wind._

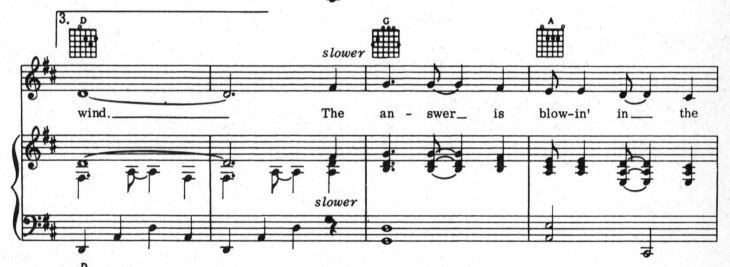

wind._ The an - swer_ is blow-in' in_ the

slower

wind._

a tempo

29

Can't Buy Me Love.

Words and music by John Lennon and Paul McCartney.

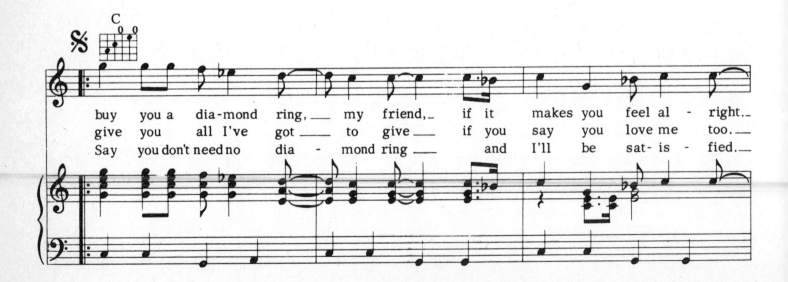

I'll get you an-y - thing, ___ my friend, ___ if it
I may not have a lot ___ to give, ___ but what I've
Tell me that you want those kind ___ of things ___ that

makes you feel al - right. ___ For I don't care too
got I'll give to you. ___ For I don't care too
mon - ey just can't buy. ___ ___ I don't care too

much for mon-ey, for mon-ey can't buy me love. ___ I'll
much for mon-ey, for mon-ey can't buy me love. ___
much for mon-ey, for mon-ey can't buy me love. ___

Can't buy me love, _____ Ev-

- 'ry - bod - y tells me so. ____ Can't buy me love, _____

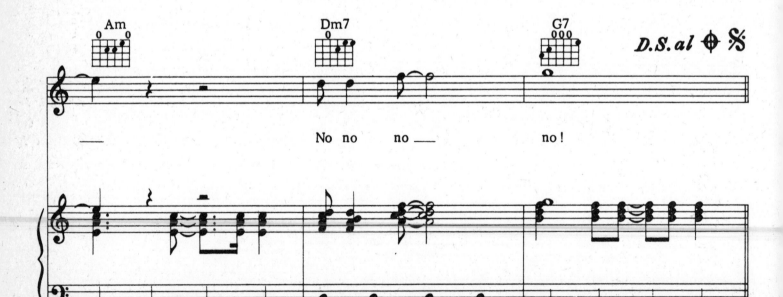

No no no _____ no!

D.S. al 𝄌 𝄋

32

Coda

Can't buy me love, _____ love.._

Can't buy me love. _____

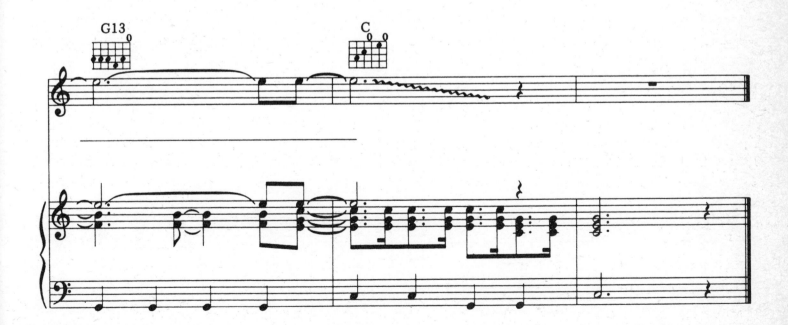

Have I The Right.

Words and music by Howard Blaikley.

Moderato

Have I the right to hold you You know I've al-ways told you That we must

nev-er ___ ev-er part Oh ___ Have I the right to kiss you

You know I'll al-ways miss you I've loved you from the ve-ry start

Catch The Wind.

Words and music by Donovan.

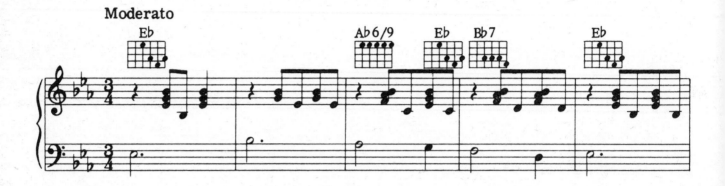

In the warm ___ hold of your lov - in' mind, ___
Ah, but I may as well try and

To catch the wind.

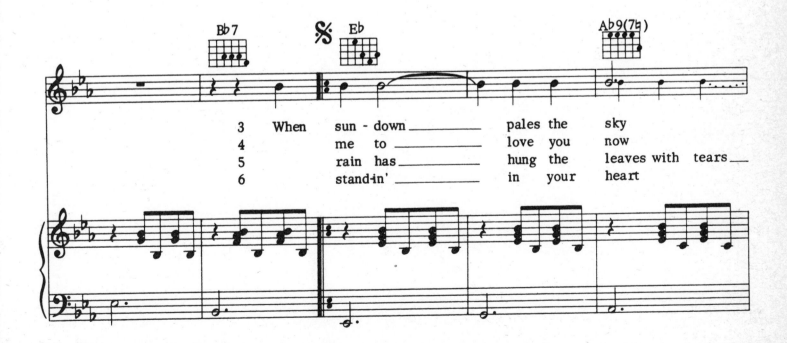

3 When sun - down ___ pales the sky
4 me to ___ love you now
5 rain has ___ hung the leaves with tears ___
6 stand-in' ___ in your heart

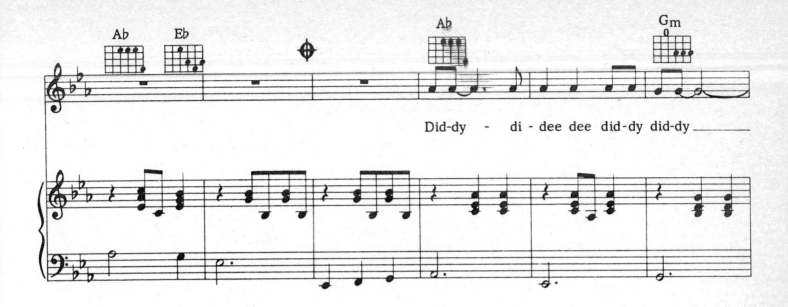

Did-dy - di - dee dee did-dy did-dy_____

did-dy did-dy _____ did-dy did-dy___ dee dee dee _____

D.S. al ⊕ %

Coda

When

Cinderella – Rockefella.

Words and music by Nancy Ames and Mason Williams.

Easy tempo

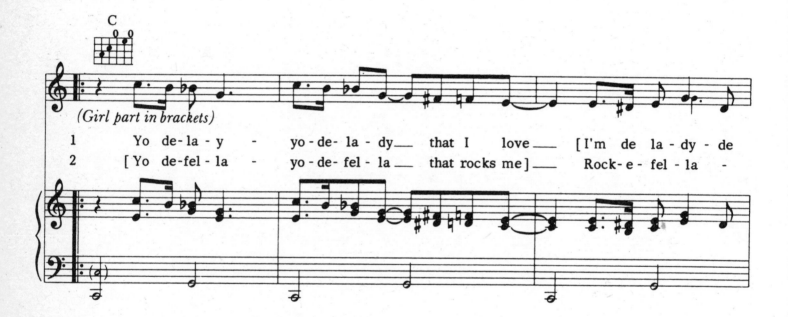

(Girl part in brackets)

1   Yo de-la-y - yode-la-dy___ that I love___ [I'm de la-dy-de

2   [Yo de-fel-la - yo-de-fel-la___ that rocks me]___ Rock-e-fel-la -

la-dy who ___   Yo-de-la-dy - yo-de-la-dy___ that I love.___

rock-e-fel-la ___   [Yo-de-fel-la - yo-de-fel-la___ that rocks me.]

[I'm de-la-dy - de la-dy who]_ Yo - de-lid - dle la-dy
Rock-e-fel-la rock-e-fel-la _ [You're my rock-e - fel-la]

[I'm de lid - dle la-dy] Oo _____ [I love your touch]_
I'm your rock-e-fel-la Oo _____ [I love your face]_

_ Thank you so much. _ I love your eyes _ [That's ve-ry nice.]_
_ 'Sin the right place. _ [I love your mind] _ That's ve-ry kind._

Classical Gas.

Mason Williams.

Slowly, ad lib.

a tempo [steady 4, with 'drive']

hold r.h. and let fade

ff *bravura*
(quasi fanfare)

46

48

Colour My World.

Words and music by Tony Hatch and Jackie Trent.

Moderato

You'll nev-er see a dark cloud hang-ing round me,____
Just as long as I know you're think-ing of me,____

Now there is on-ly blue sky to sur-round me,____
There'll be a rain-bow al-ways up a-bove me,____

There's nev-er been a grey day since you found me._____
Since I found the one who real-ly loves me._____

Ev - 'ry - thing I touch is turn-ing to gold._____ So, you can

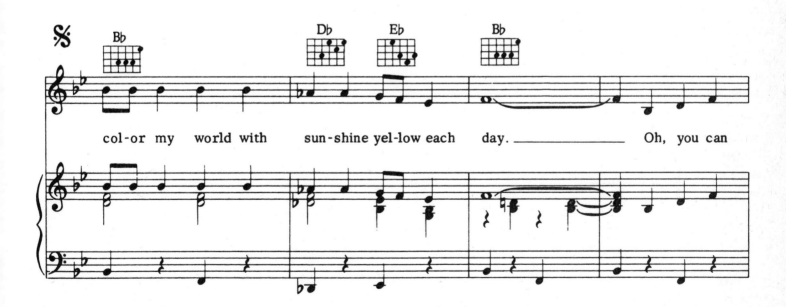

col-or my world with sun-shine yel-low each day._____ Oh, you can

col-or my world with hap-pi-ness all the way. _____ Just take the

green from the grass and the blue from the sky up a-bove, _____ And if you

col-or my world, just paint it with your love. _____ Just col-or my

world. _____

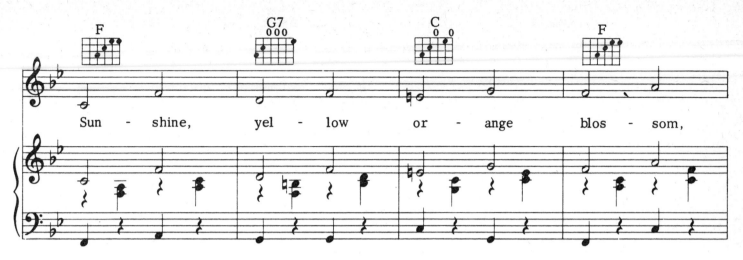

Sun - shine, yel - low or - ange blos - som,

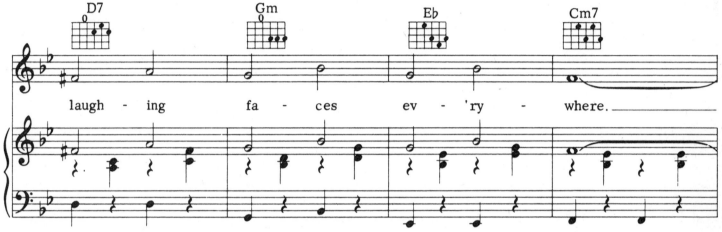

laugh - ing fa - ces ev - 'ry - where.

D.S. al ⊕ 𝄋   ⊕ *Coda*

So you can   world.

Just col-or my world, _____ Just col-or my world.

(They Long To Be)
Close To You.

Music by Burt Bacharach.
Words by Hal David.

Moderato

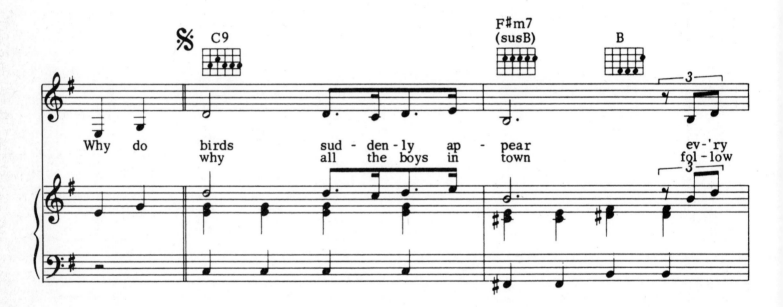

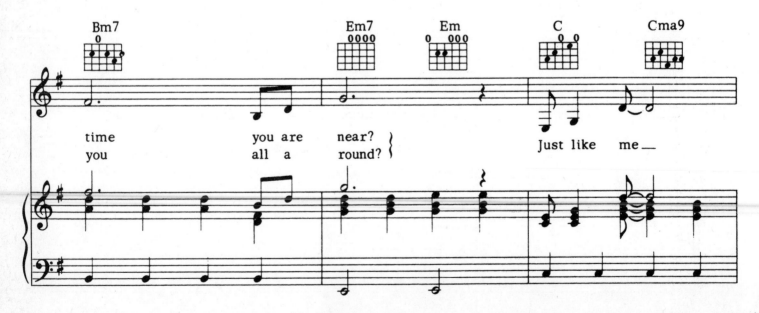

they long   to   be   close to   you. _____   Why do

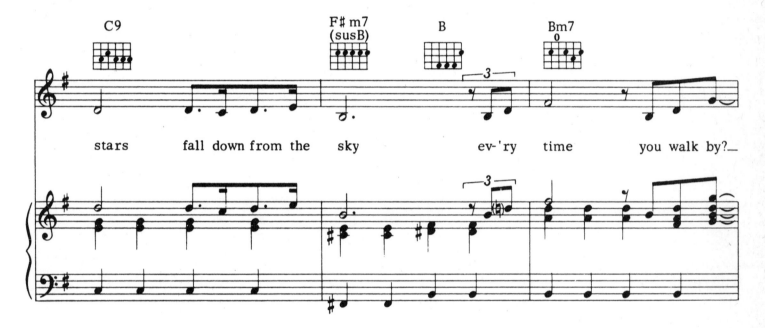

stars   fall down from the sky   ev-'ry time   you walk by?__

____   Just like   me __   they long   to   be

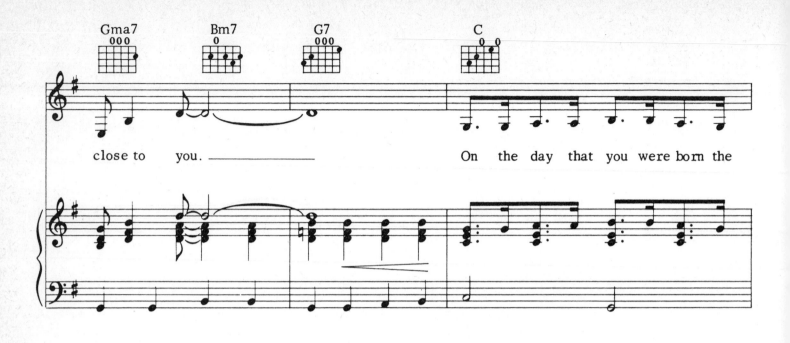

close to you. _____ On the day that you were born the

an - gels got to - ge - ther___ And de - ci - ded to cre - ate a dream come

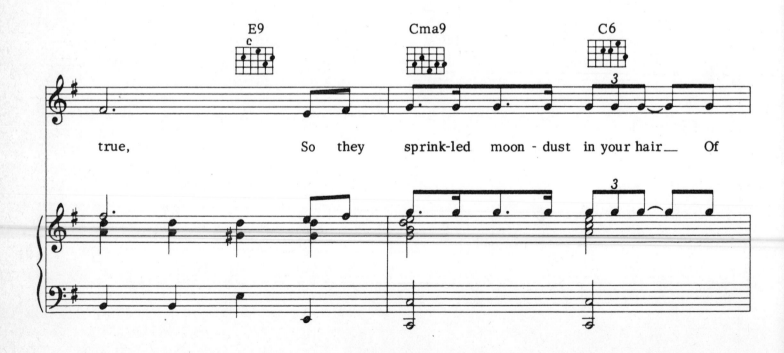

true, So they sprink-led moon - dust in your hair___ Of

gold, and star-light in your eyes of blue. That is

D.S. al ⊕ 𝄉

⊕ *Coda*

close to you._____ Ah _____

repeat and fade

Close to you._____

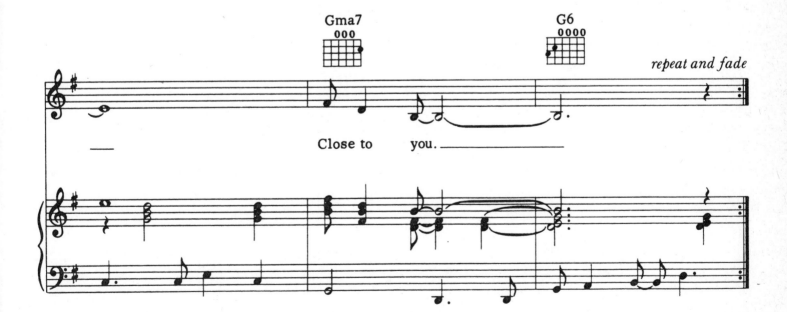

Can't Help Falling In Love.

Words and music by George Weiss, Hugo Peretti and Luigi Creatore.

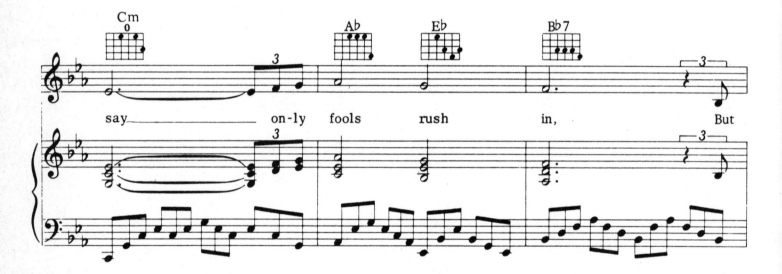

you.   Shall   I   stay, _____ would it

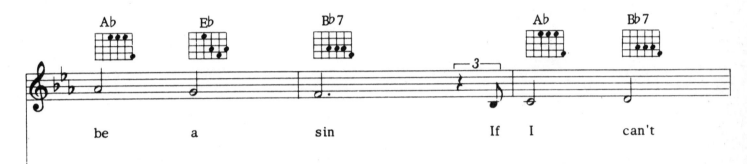

be   a   sin   If   I   can't

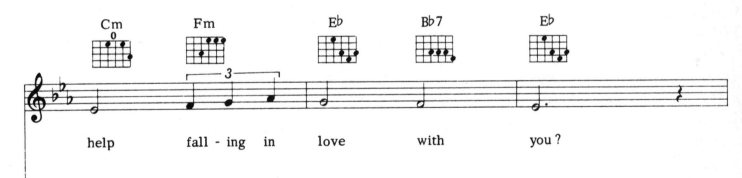

help   fall - ing   in   love   with   you ?

like a riv-er flows sure-ly to the sea, Dar-ling, so it goes,

some things ___ are meant to be. Take my

hand, _____ take my whole life too, For

I can't help fall-ing in love with you.

Eleanor Rigby.

Words and music by John Lennon and Paul McCartney.

Moderately, with a steady beat

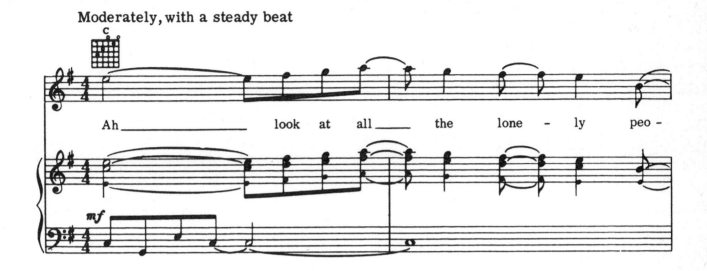

Ah _____ look at all ___ the lone - ly peo -

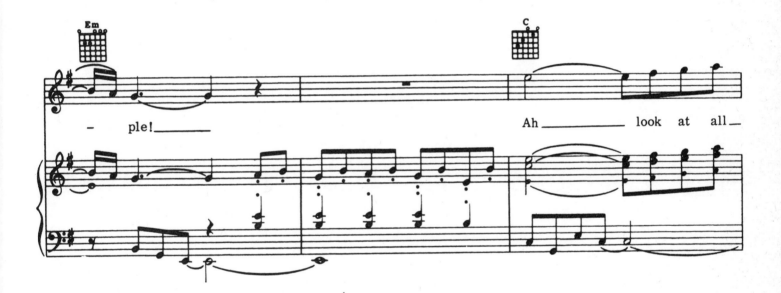

- ple! _____ Ah _____ look at all__

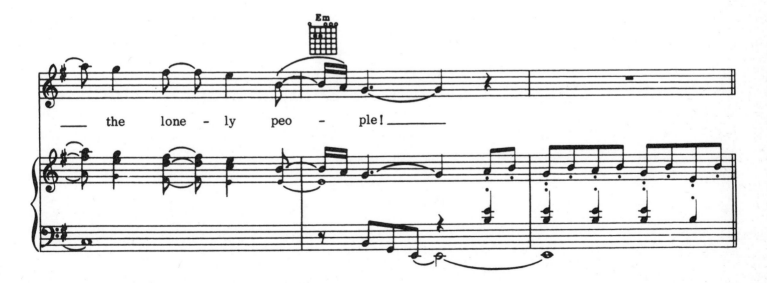

___ the lone - ly peo - ple! _____

1. E-lea-nor Rig - by, picks up the rice___ in the church_where a wed - ding has been,___
2. Fath-er Mc Ken - zie, writ - ing the words_ of a ser - mon that no - one will hear,___
3. E - lea-nor Rig - by, died in the church_ and was bur - ied a - long with her name,___

___ lives in a dream._____ Waits at the win - dow,
___ no one comes near._____ Look at him work - ing,
___ no - bod - y came._____ Fa - ther Mc Ken - zie,

wear - ing the face__ that she keeps__ in a jar__ by the door,___
darn - ing his socks_ in the night__ when there's no - bod - y there,___
wip - ing the dirt__from his hands__ as he walks_ from the grave,___

I Saw Her Standing There.

Words and music by John Lennon and Paul McCartney.

Well she was

just se-ven - teen,___ You know what I mean,___ And the
she looked at me, ___ And- I, I could see ___ That be-

way she looked_ was way be-yond com - pare. _____ So
fore too long___ I'd fall in love with her. _____

how   could I   dance___   with a - no - ther.___   Oh ___ when I
She   would-n't   dance___   with a - no - ther.___   Oh ___ when I

saw   her   stan - ding there.   Well
saw   her   stan - ding there.   Well my

heart   went   zoom   when I   cross'd   that   room,   And I

held   her   hand   in   mine. _____

_____   Oh   we danced ___   through the   night ___   And we

held   each o-ther   tight, ___   And be-fore too long ___   I   fell   in love with

her. _____ Now I'll ne-ver dance___ with a - no-

ther. Oh, _____ when I saw her stan - ding

there. _____ Since I there. _____

Don't Sleep In The Subway.

Words and music by Tony Hatch and Jackie Trent.

Medium beat

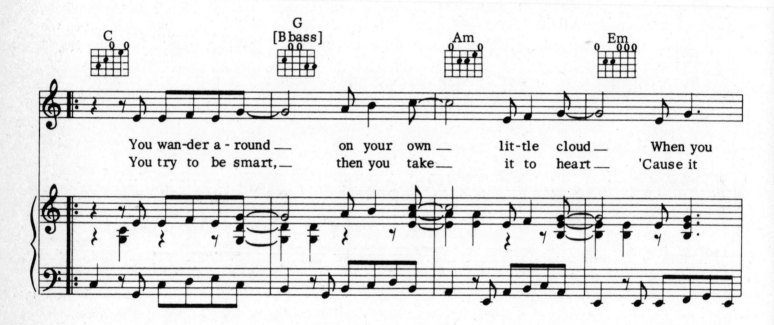

You wan-der a-round ___ on your own ___ lit-tle cloud ___ When you
You try to be smart, ___ then you take ___ it to heart ___ 'Cause it

don't see ___ the why ___ or the where - fore. _____
hurts when ___ your e - go's de-fla - ted. _____

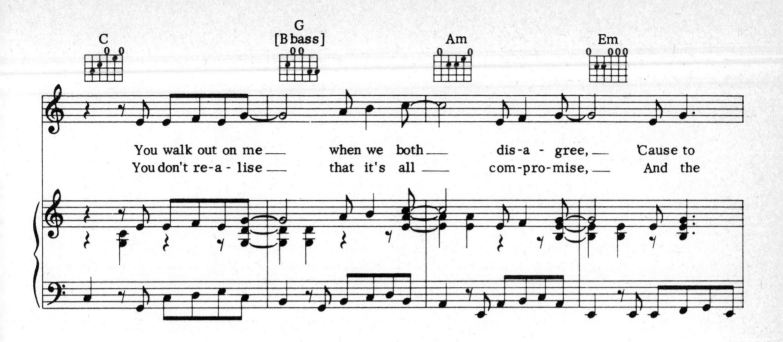

You walk out on me ___ when we both ___ dis-a-gree, ___ 'Cause to
You don't re-a-lise ___ that it's all ___ com-pro-mise, ___ And the

rea - son is not what you care ___ for. ___
prob-lems are so ov-er-ra - ted. ___

I've heard it all a mil - lion times be - fore,
Good-bye means no - thing when it's all for show,

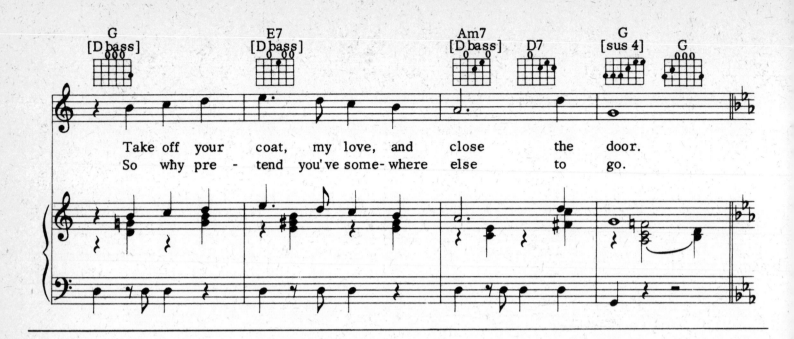

Take off your coat, my love, and close the door.
So why pre - tend you've some-where else to go.

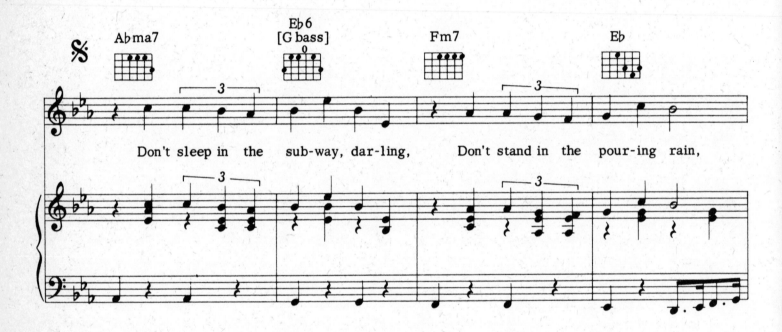

Don't sleep in the sub-way, dar-ling, Don't stand in the pour-ing rain,

Don't sleep in the sub-way, dar-ling, the night is long.— For-get your fool-ish pride,

no-thing's wrong___ now you're be-side___ me a - gain.

gain.

D.S. al ✛ ℅

✛ *Coda*

gain.___

rit.

Down Town.

Words and music by Tony Hatch.

Copyright © 1964 by ATV Music Ltd., London W1 for the World.
International Copyright Secured. All Rights Reserved.

1. When you're a - lone___ and life is mak - ing you lone - ly, you can
2. Don't hang a - round___ and let your prob - lems sur - round___ you, there are
3. *(Instrumental to *)*

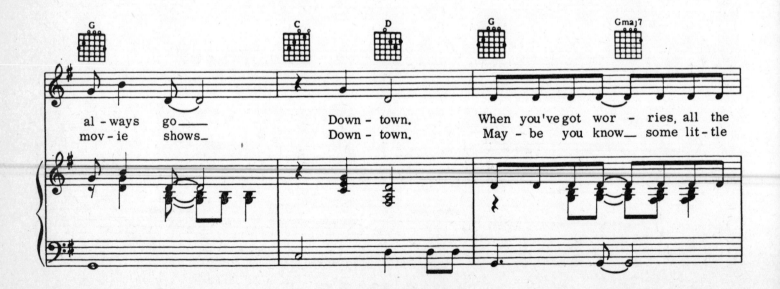

al - ways   go___   Down - town.   When you've got wor - ries, all the
mov - ie   shows___   Down - town.   May - be   you know___ some lit - tle

noise and the hur - ry seems to help, I know.___ Down - town. Just
plac-es to go___ to where they nev - er close.___ Down - town. Just
                                                              * And

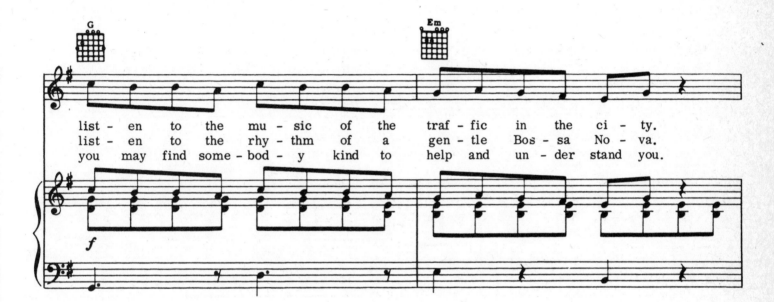

list - en to the mu - sic of the traf - fic in the ci - ty.
list - en to the rhy - thm of a gen - tle Bos - sa No - va.
you may find some - bod - y kind to help and un - der stand you.

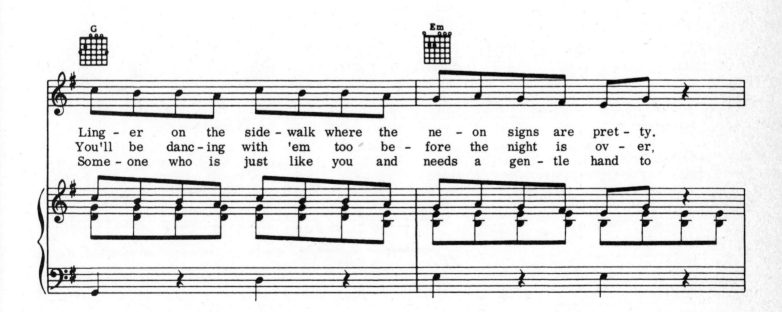

Ling - er on the side - walk where the ne - on signs are pret - ty.
You'll be danc - ing with 'em too be - fore the night is ov - er,
Some - one who is just like you and needs a gen - tle hand to

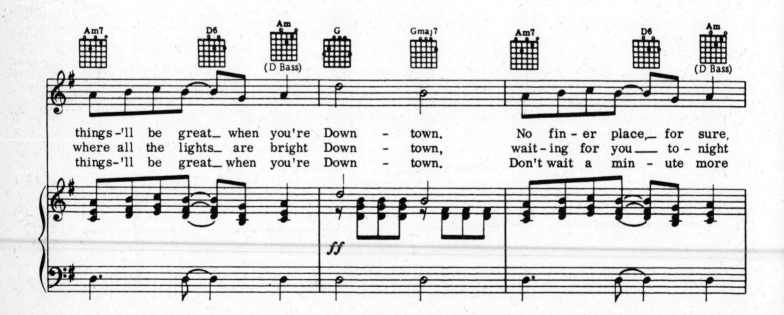

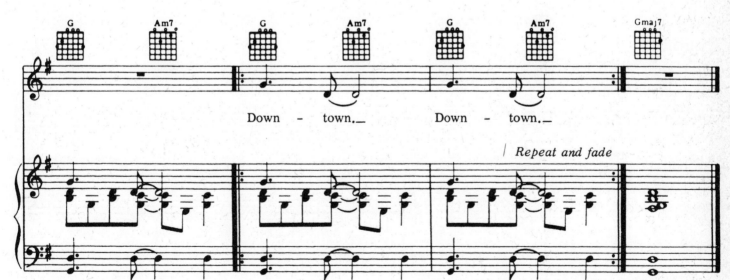

Everybody's Talkin'.

Words and music by Fred Neil.

Moderately

Eve-ry-bod-y's Talk-in' at me I don't hear a word they're say-in'

On-ly the ech-oes___ of my mind._____ Peo-ple

stop-pin' star-in'   I can't   see   the fac-es   On-ly   the sha-dows___ of their

eyes._____   I'm   go-in' where the   sun___   keeps shin-in'

thru the pour-in'   rain   Go-in' where the wea-ther___   suits my

clothes_____   Bank-in' off of the north-east wind   Sail-in' on a sum-mer

breeze   Skip-pin' o-ver the o-cean like a   stone._____

Eve-ry-bod-y's   Talk-in' at me   I don't hear a word they're say-in'

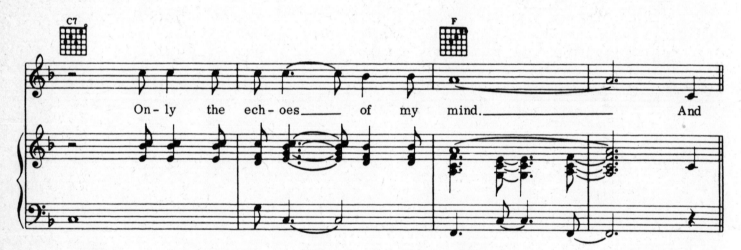

On-ly the ech-oes_____ of my mind._____ And

Repeat and Fade

I won't let you leave my love_____ be-hind _____   No,
I won't let you leave my love_____ be-hind _____   And,
I won't let you leave my love_____ be-hind._____

Fire And Rain.

By James Taylor.

Slow rock

Verse

Just yes-ter-day morn-in' they let me know ____ you were gone, ____

Su-san, the plans they made put an end to you. I walked out this morn-in' and I

But I   al - ways thought that I'd see   you   a - gain.

2 Won't you look down upon me, Jesus, you got to help me make a stand;
   You just got to see me through another day.
   My body's achin' and my time is at hand,
   An' I won't make it any other way.
      [Chorus]

3 Been walkin' my mind to an easy time, my back turned towards the sun.
   Lord knows when the cold wind blows it'll turn your head around.
   Well, there's hours of time on the telephone line to talk about things to come,
   Sweet dreams and flying machines in pieces on the ground.
      [Chorus]

The Fool On The Hill.

Words and music by John Lennon and Paul McCartney.

perfect-ly still,   But   no-bo-dy wants to know__ him,__ they can
perfect-ly loud,   But   no-bo-dy ev - er hears__ him,__ or the
                     And   no-bo-dy seems to like __ him,__ they can
                     He nev-er list - ens to __ them,__ he __

5th time fade

see that he's just a fool,_____   And he nev-er gives an an - swer, But the
sound he ap-pears to make,_____   And he nev-er seems to no - tice, But the
tell what he wants to do, _____   And he nev-er shows his feel - ings, But the
knows that they're the fools. __   They don't like __ him, The

fool ___ on the hill ___ sees the sun go-ing down, ___ And the

eyes in his head ___ see the world ___ spin-ning round. ___

From Both Sides, Now.

Words and music by Joni Mitchell.

Moderately *(with a light beat)*

1. Bows and flows of an-gel hair,___ and ice cream cas-tles in the air,___ and
2. Moons and Junes and fer-ris wheels,___ the diz-zy danc-ing way you feel,___ as
3. Tears and fears and feel-ing proud,___ to say "I love you" right out loud,___

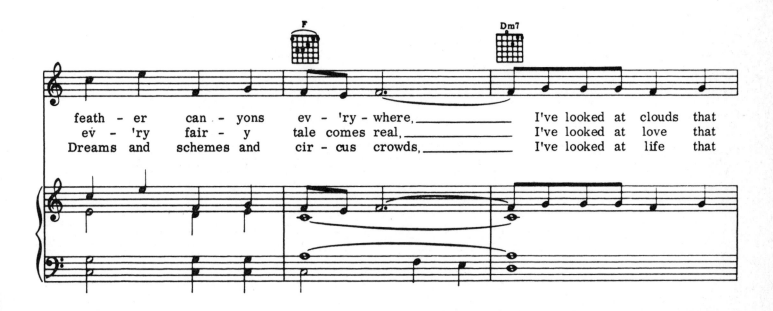

feath-er can-yons ev-'ry-where,_____ I've looked at clouds that
ev-'ry fair-y tale comes real,_____ I've looked at love that
Dreams and schemes and cir-cus crowds,_____ I've looked at life that

way. But now they on - ly block the sun,___ they
way. But now it's just an - oth - er show,___ you
way. But now old friends are act - ing strange,_ they

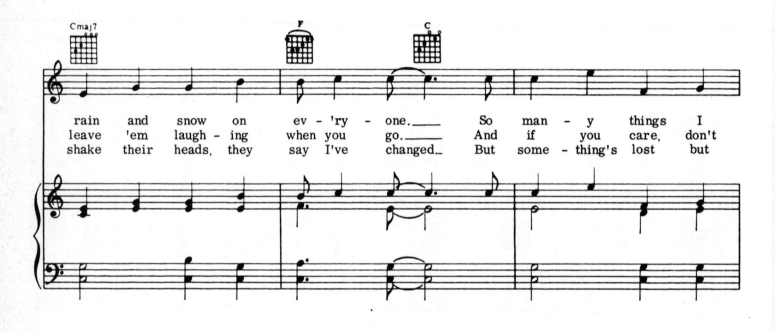

rain and snow on ev - 'ry - one.___ So man - y things I
leave 'em laugh - ing when you go.___ And if you care, don't
shake their heads, they say I've changed._ But some - thing's lost but

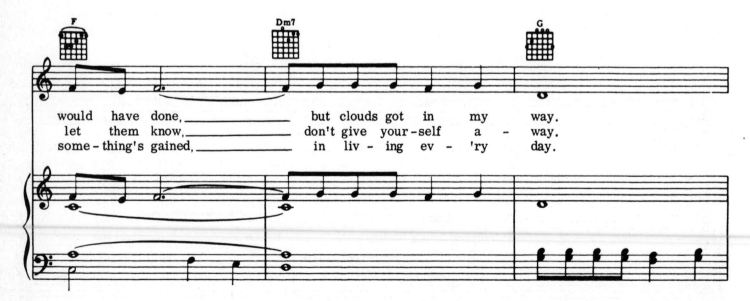

would have done,_____ but clouds got in my way.
let them know,_____ don't give your - self a - way.
some - thing's gained,_____ in liv - ing ev - 'ry day.

I've looked at clouds from both sides now,___ from up and down___ and
I've looked at love from both sides now,___ from give and take___ and
I've looked at life from both sides now,___ from win and lose___ and

still some-how___ it's cloud il-lu-sions I re-call; I real-ly___ don't know
still some-how___ it's love's il-lu-sions I re-call; I real-ly___ don't know
still some-how___ it's life's il-lu-sions I re-call; I real-ly___ don't know

clouds_____ at___ all._____
love _____ at___ . all._____
life _____ at___ all._____

1.

2.

Repeat and fade out

Sunny.

Words and music by Bobby Hebb.

Get Back.

Words and music by John Lennon and Paul McCartney.

32 bars per minute

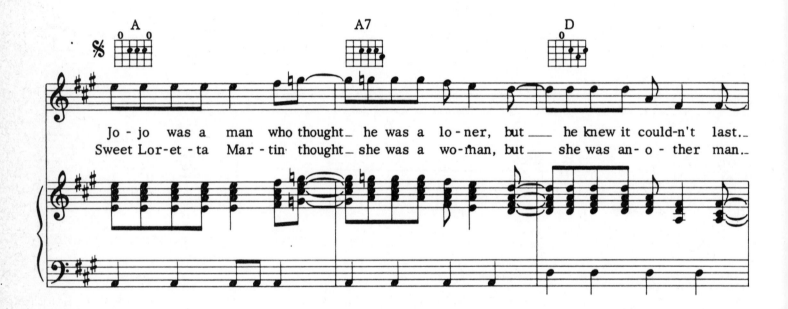

Jo - jo was a man who thought he was a lo - ner, but he knew it could-n't last.

Sweet Lor-et - ta Mar - tin thought she was a wo-man, but she was an-o - ther man.

Jo - jo left his home in Tu - scon, A - ri - zo - na, for

All the girls a - round her say she's got it com-ing, but

The Mood I'm In.

Words and music by Pete King and Paul Francis Webster.

Brightly

1. I like to feel fan-cy free, I like to live young. I like the old mer-ry-go-
2. I like to hear op-'ra or I like to read Joyce I'm not the pre-dict-a-ble

F   Cm7   F   Cm7   F   Cm7

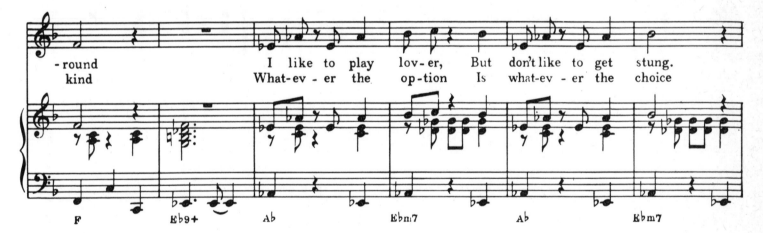

-round I like to play lov-er, But don't like to get stung.
kind What-ev-er the op-tion Is what-ev-er the choice

F   Eb9+   Ab   Ebm7   Ab   Ebm7

I like my two feet on the ground I may date a girl light-ly and
I like to make up my own mind If the choice were to break up or

Ab   Gm7-5   Gm7   C7   F   Gm7

A Hard Day's Night.

Words and music by John Lennon and Paul McCartney.

sleep-ing ___   like a log, ___   But when I
give me ___   ev-'ry-thing; ___   So why I

get home to you ___ I find the things that you do ___ Will make me
love to come home, ___ 'Cos when I get you a - lone ___ You know I

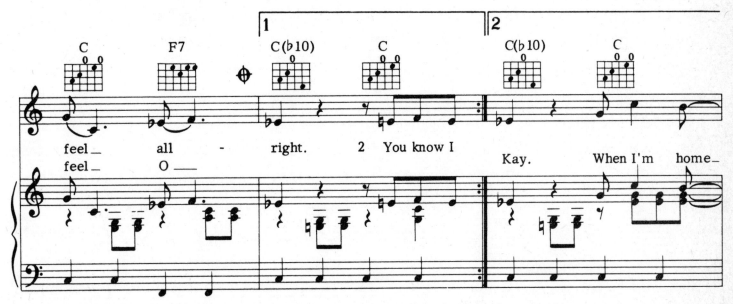

feel ___ all - right.   2 You know I
feel ___ O ___   Kay.   When I'm home ___

Hey Jude.

Words and music by John Lennon and Paul McCartney.

Hey Jude,_____ don't make it bad, take a

sad song__ and make it bet-ter.__ Re-mem-ber to let her in-to your

heart, then you can start_____ to make it__ bet - ter.__ Hey

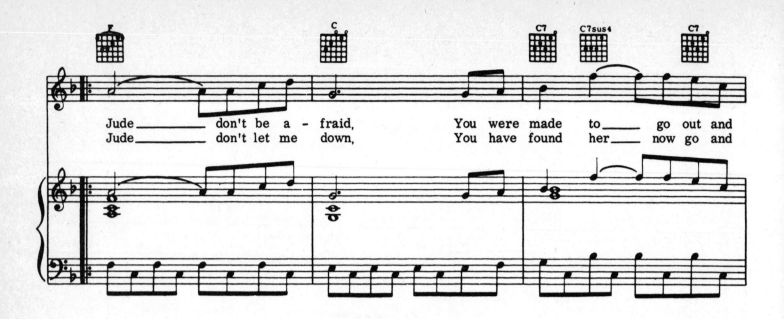

Jude_____ don't be a - fraid,   You were made to_____ go out and
Jude_____ don't let me down,   You have found her_____ now go and

get her._____   The min - ute   you let her un - der your
get her._____   Re - mem - ber   to let her in - to your

skin,   then you be - gin_____ to make it_____ bet - ter._____
heart,   then you can start_____ to make it_____ bet - ter._____

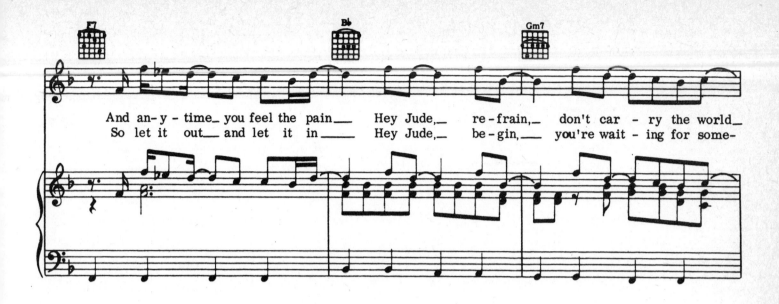

And an-y-time you feel the pain___ Hey Jude,___ re-frain,___ don't car-ry the world___
So let it out___ and let it in___ Hey Jude,___ be-gin,___ you're wait-ing for some-

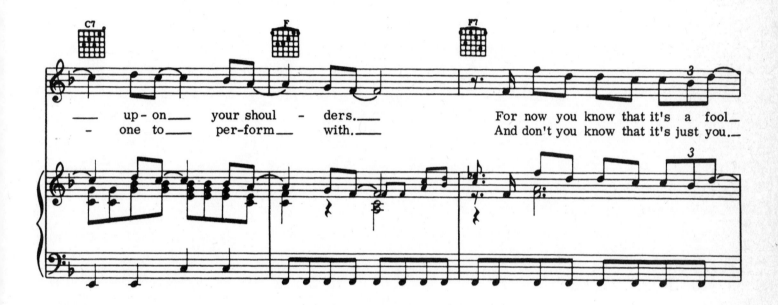

___ up-on___ your shoul - ders.___ For now you know that it's a fool___
___ one to___ per-form___ with.___ And don't you know that it's just you.___

___ who plays___ it cool___ By mak-ing his world___ a lit-tle___ cold-
___ Hey Jude,___ you'll do.___ The move-ment you need___ is on___ your___ shoul-

er._____ Da da da da___ da da da da da.
der._____ Da da da da___ da da da da da.

Hey   Hey___ Jude,_____ don't make it

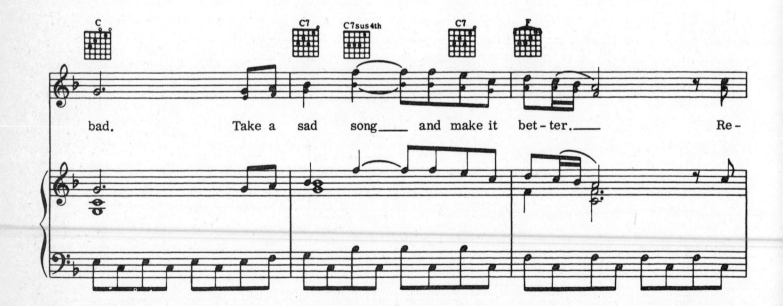

bad.   Take a sad song___ and make it bet-ter.___   Re-

mem - ber   to let her un - der your skin,   then you'll be - gin___   to make it   bet -

- ter, bet - ter, bet - ter, bet - ter, bet - ter, bet - ter, Oh_____ Yeh yeh yeh yeh yeh yeh yeh

Da da da da   Da da da da   Hey___ Jude

Repeat till Fade with effects.

Da   da   da   da da da da   da da da da   Hey___ Jude.

He Ain't Heavy...
He's My Brother.

Lyrics by Bob Russell.
Music by Bobby Scott.

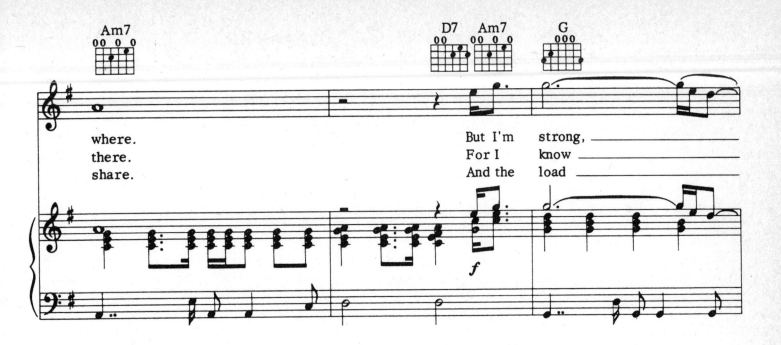

where.
there.
share.

But I'm strong, _____
For I know _____
And the load _____

___ strong e - nough to car - ry him.
___ he would not en - cum - ber me.
___ does-n't weigh me down ___ at all.

He ain't heavy,

He's my bro-ther. ___

So on we

If I'm

la-den__ at all, __ I'm la-den__ with sad - ness__ that

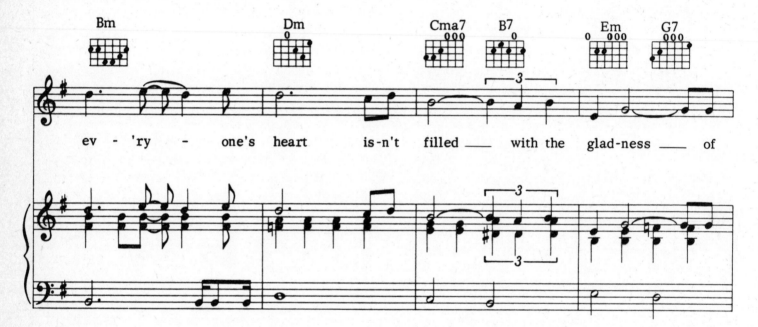

ev - 'ry - one's heart is-n't filled __ with the glad-ness __ of

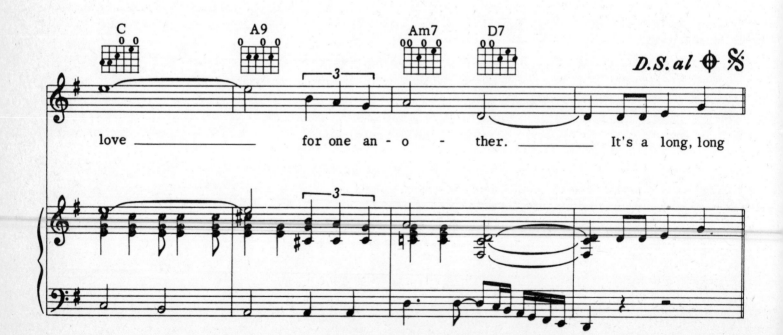

love _____ for one an - o - ther. _____ It's a long, long

D.S. al ⊕ 𝄌

I Close My Eyes And Count To Ten.

Words and music by Clive Westlake

Moderato

It is-n't the way that you look, and it is-n't the way that you

talk; It is-n't the things that you say or do make me want you so.
(show;)

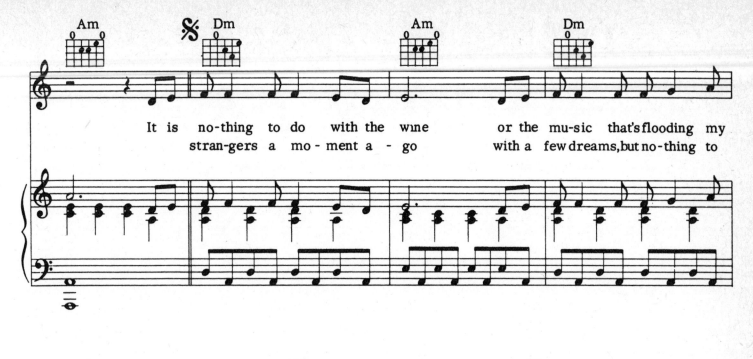

It is no-thing to do with the wine or the mu-sic that's flooding my
stran-gers a mo-ment a-go with a few dreams, but no-thing to

mind, And nev-er be-fore have I been so sure you're the
show. The world was a place with a frown on its face, and to-

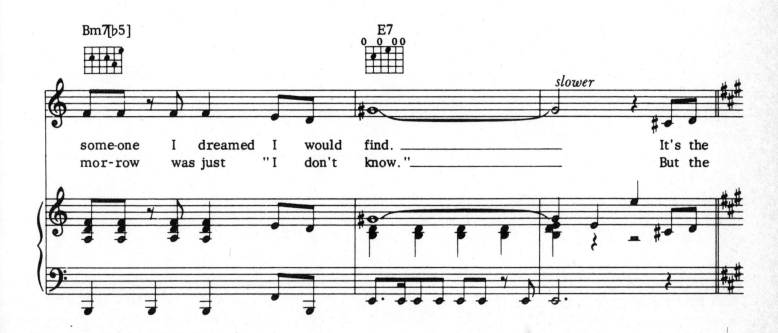

some-one I dreamed I would find. _____ It's the
mor-row was just "I don't know." _____ But the

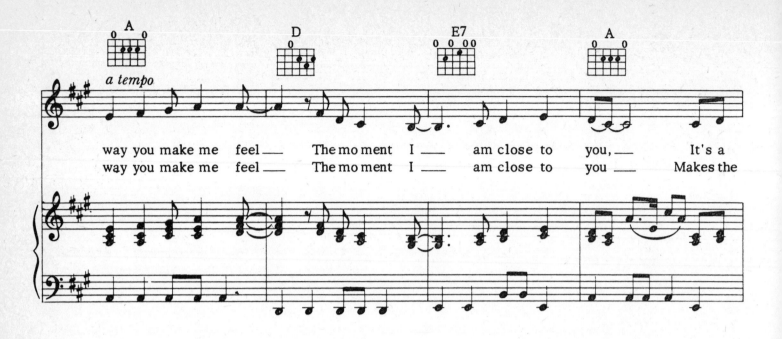

way you make me feel ___ The mo ment I ___ am close to you, ___ It's a
way you make me feel ___ The mo ment I ___ am close to you ___ Makes the

feel-ing so un - real, ___ Some-how I can't ___ be-lieve it's true. ___ The
day seem so un - real, ___ Some-how I can't ___ be-lieve it's true. ___ To -

poun-ding I feel in my heart, The hop-ing that we'll nev-er part. I
mor-row will you still be here, To - mor-row will come, but I fear That

can't be-lieve this is real - ly happ'ning to me.
what is happ- 'ning to me is on-ly a dream.

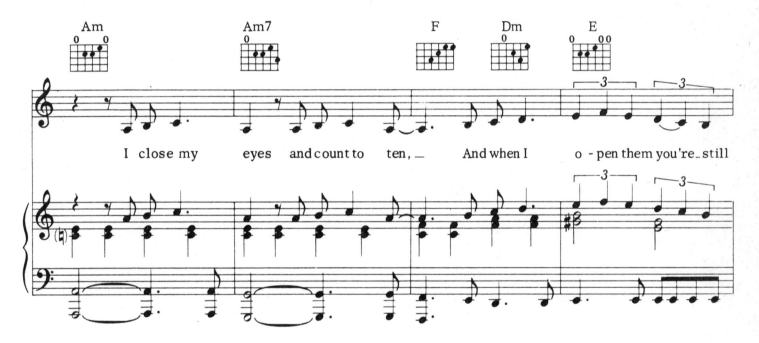

I close my eyes and count to ten, __ And when I o - pen them you're still

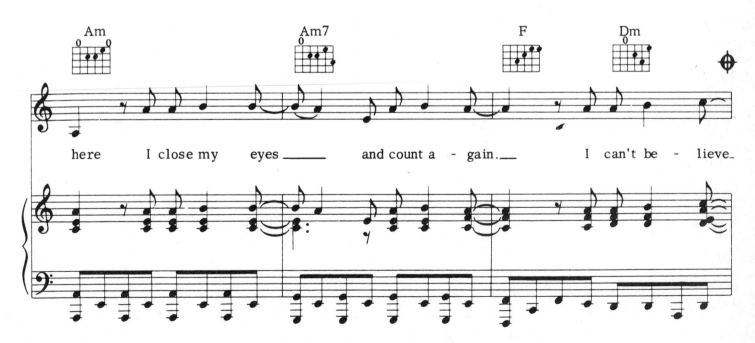

here I close my eyes ____ and count a - gain.__ I can't be - lieve__

it, but you're still here. We were

_____ it, but you're still _____

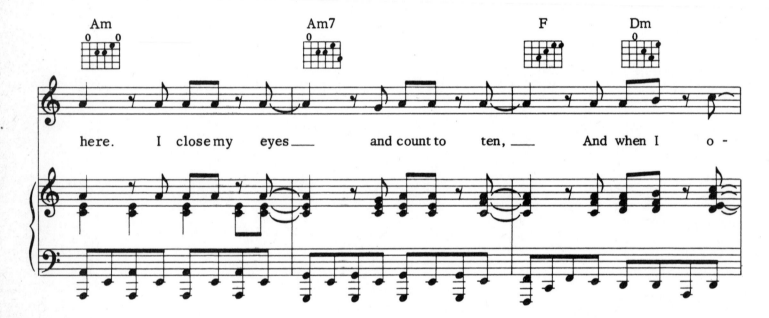

here. I close my eyes _____ and count to ten, _____ And when I o-

- pen them you're still _____ here. _____

Glad All Over.

Words and music by Dave Clark and Mike Smith.

Moderato

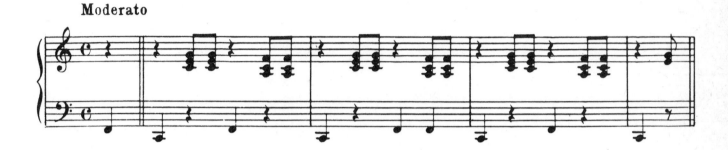

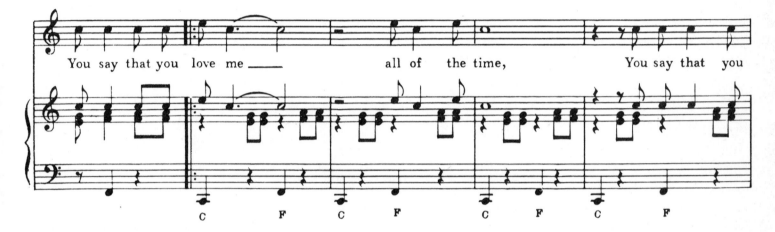

You say that you love me ___ all of the time, You say that you

need me ___ you'll al-ways be mine. I'm feel-in' glad all ov-

-er, glad all ov-er. Ba-by I'm glad all ov-er so glad you're

But you know here by your side I will stay, I - I - I'll stay. Our love will

last now _____ till the end of time. Be-cause this

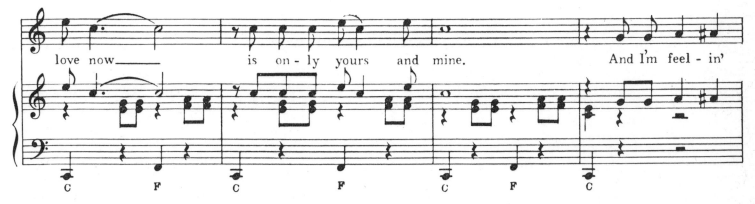

love now _____ is on-ly yours and mine. And I'm feel-in'

glad all ov - er, _____ glad all ov - er, Ba-by I'm glad all ov-

- er, so glad you're mine. So say that you mine. _____

I Just Don't Know What To Do With Myself.

Music By Burt Bacharach.
Words By Hal David.

Slowly

I just don't know what to do with my-self, Don't know just what to do with my-self. I'm so used to do-ing ev-'ry-thing with you, Plan-ning

ev-'ry-thing for two, And now that we're through I just don't know what to do with my-

time. I'm so lone-some for you It a crime, Go-ing to a mo - vie

on-ly makes me sad, Par-ties make me feel it bad when I'm not with you.

I just don't know what to do. _____ Like a sum - mer rose _____

_____ needs the sun and _ rain _____ I need your sweet love to beat _ all the

pain. _____ I just don't know what to do with my - self, _____ I just don't

I Love You Because.

Words and music by Leon Payne.

Moderato

I love you be - cause you un - der - stand, dear, _____
love you be - cause my heart is ligh - ter _____

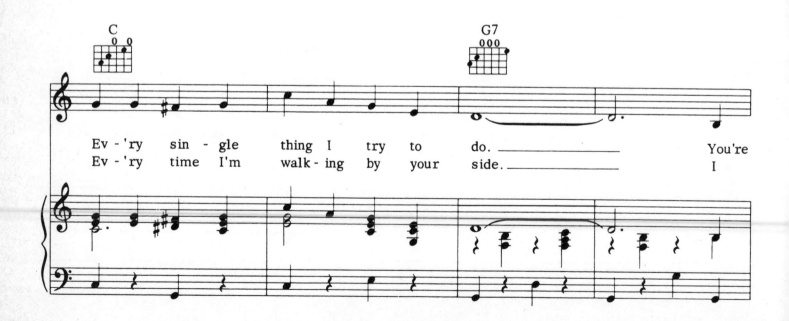

Ev - 'ry sin - gle thing I try to do. _____ You're
Ev - 'ry time I'm walk - ing by your side. _____ I

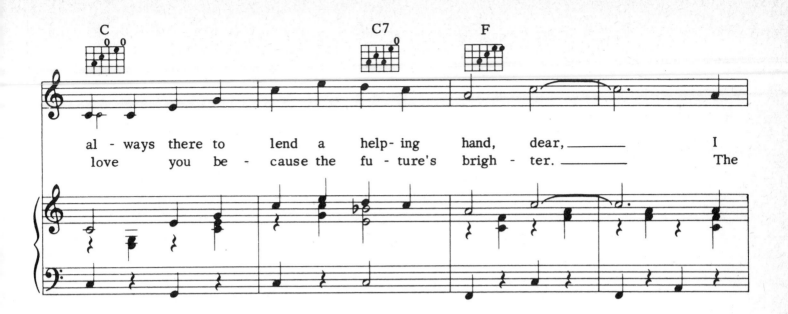

al - ways there to lend a help- ing hand, dear,_____ I
love you be - cause the fu - ture's brigh - ter._____ The

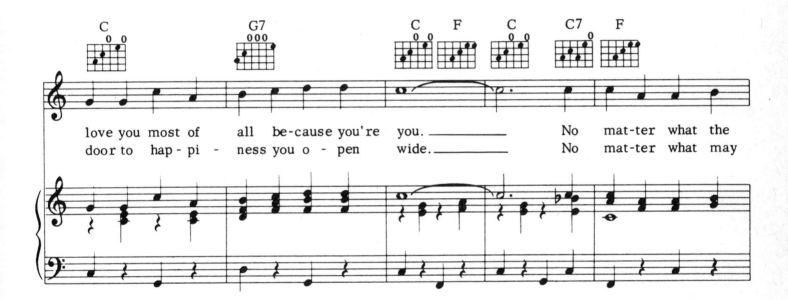

love you most of all be-cause you're you._____ No mat-ter what the
door to hap - pi - ness you o - pen wide._____ No mat-ter what may

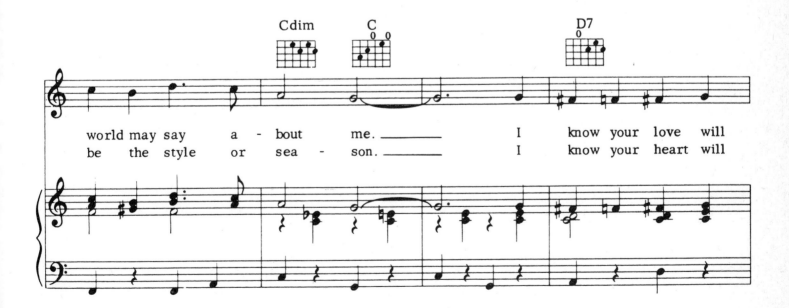

world may say a - bout me._____ I know your love will
be the style or sea - son._____ I know your heart will

al - ways see me through. _____ I love you for the
al - ways be true. _____ I love you for a

way you nev - er doubt me, _____ But most of all I
hun - dred thou - sand rea - sons, _____ But most of all I

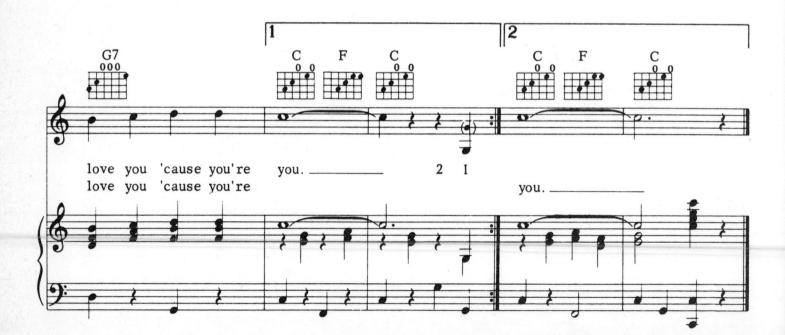

love you 'cause you're you. _____ 2 I
love you 'cause you're you. _____

If My Friends Could See Me Now.

Words by Dorothy Fields.
Music by Cy Coleman.

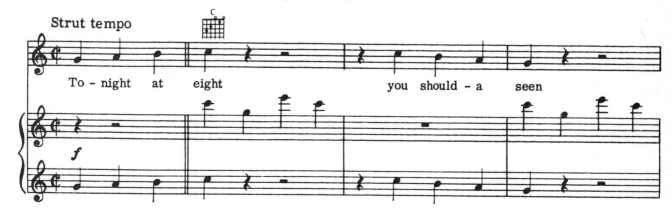

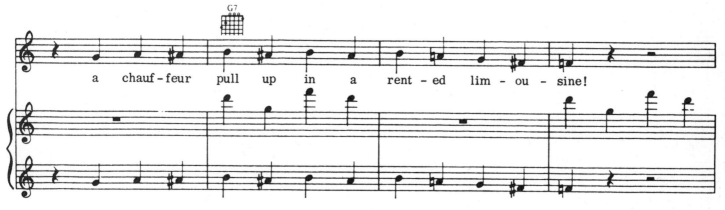

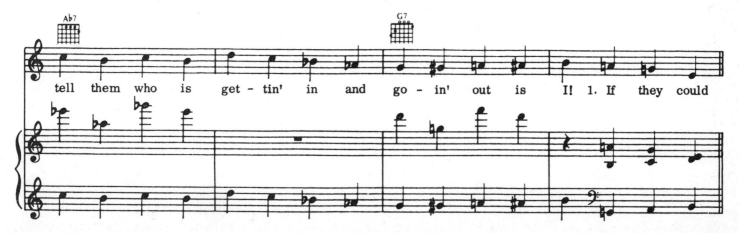

I Want To Hold Your Hand.

Words and music by John Lennon and Paul McCartney.

Moderately, with a beat

Oh yeh, I'll _____ tell you some-thing I think you'll un-der-

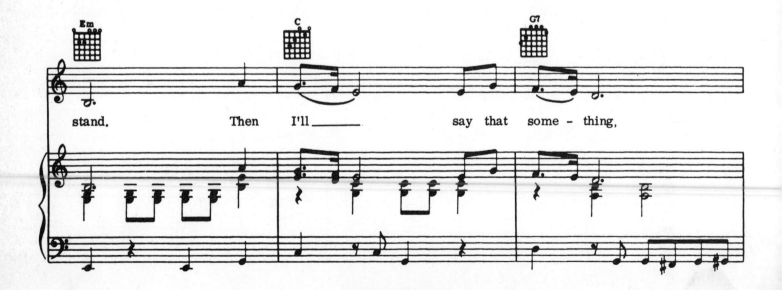

stand. Then I'll _____ say that some-thing,

I Want To Hold Your Hand.____ I Want To Hold Your

Hand._____ I Want To Hold Your Hand.____ Oh____

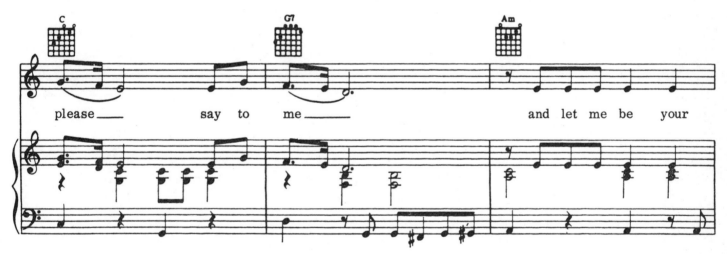

please____ say to me_____ and let me be your

man, and please____ say to me_____

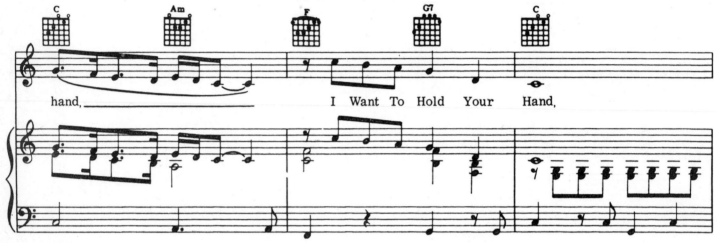

I Want To Hold Your Hand,_____

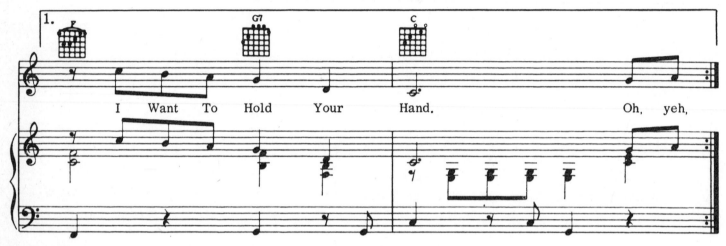

1. I Want To Hold Your Hand. Oh, yeh,

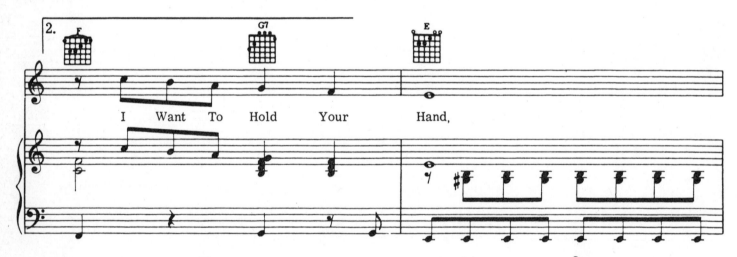

2. I Want To Hold Your Hand,

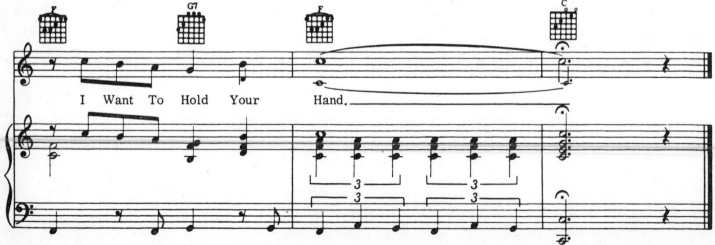

I Want To Hold Your Hand._____

I, Who Have Nothing.

English lyric by Jerry Leiber and Mike Stoller.
Music by C. Donida.

Slowly

I,   I who have no-thing,   I,   I who have

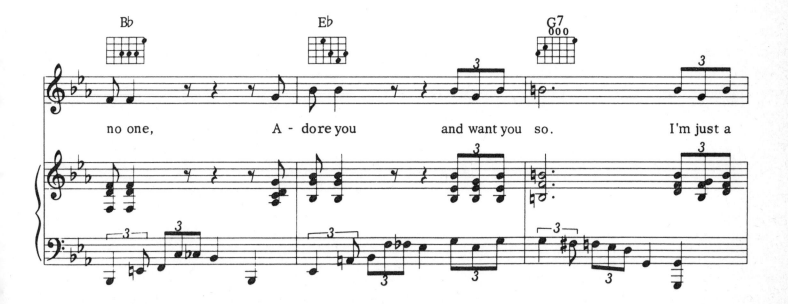

no one,   A - dore you   and want you so.   I'm just a

no-one   with no-thing to give you, but,   Oh,   I love you.

He,   he buys you dia-monds,

Bright,   spar-kling dia-monds,   But be-lieve me,   dear, when I

say   that he can   give you the world,but he'll nev-er   love you the

way   I   love you.   He can

take you an-y place he wants,_   To   fan - cy clubs and res-tau-rants,_ But

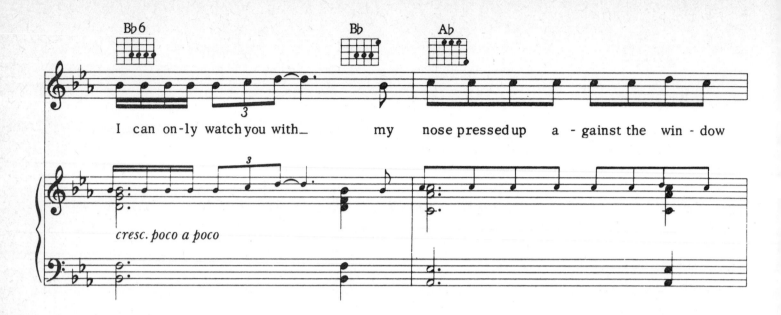

I can on-ly watch you with__ my nose pressed up a-gainst the win-dow

cresc. poco a poco

pane. _____

mf _____

f

I, I who have no-thing, I, I who have

no one,   Must watch you   go dan-cing by,   Wrapped in the

arms of somebod-y else, when dar-ling, it is I   who love you.

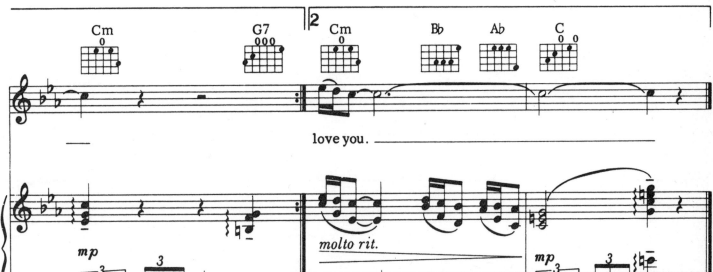

love you.

I Will Wait For You.

English lyric by Norman Gimbel.
Music by Michel Legrand.

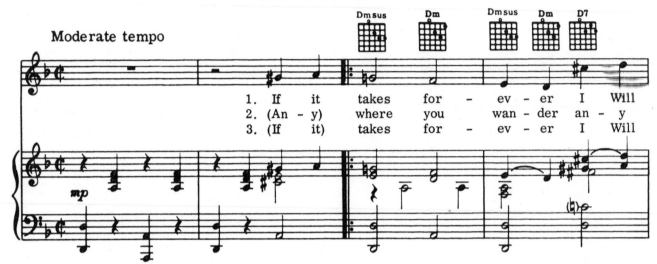

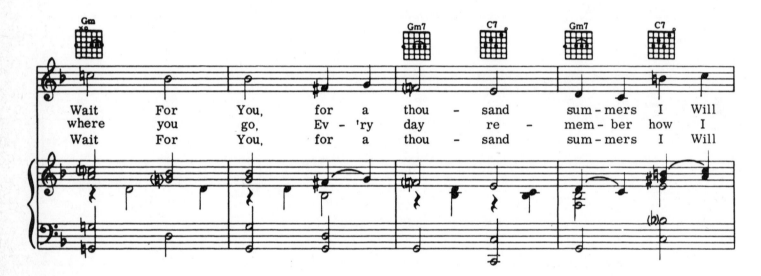

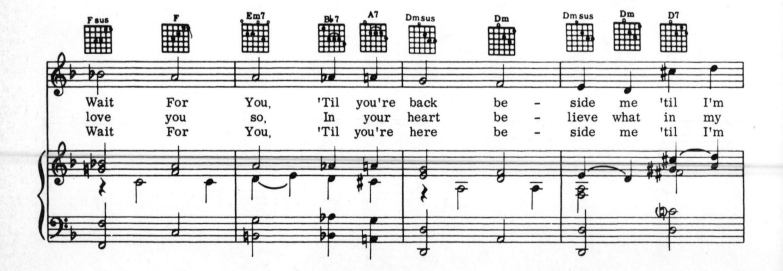

1. If it takes for - ev - er I Will Wait For You, for a thou - sand sum - mers I Will Wait For You, 'Til you're back be - side me 'til I'm
2. (An - y) where you wan - der an - y where you go, Ev - 'ry day re - mem - ber how I love you so, In your heart be - lieve what in my
3. (If it) takes for - ev - er I Will Wait For You, for a thou - sand sum - mers I Will Wait For You, 'Til you're here be - side me 'til I'm

hold - ing you 'til I hear you sigh
heart I know that for - ev - er more
touch - ing you and for - ev - er more

here in my arms.
I'll wait for 2. An - y
shar - ing your

2. *Ahead to Interlude*

you. _____ The love. _____

3.

Fine

Interlude

Jumpin' Jack Flash.

Words and music by Mick Jagger and Keith Richard.

Brightly

I was
I was
I was

born	in a	cross-fire	*hur-ri-	cane,	
raised	by a	tooth-less bear-ded	hag.	
drowned,	I was	washed up and left	for	dead.

And I howled at my Ma in the dri - ving rain.
I was schooled with a strap right a - cross my back.
I fell down to my feet and I saw they bled.

But it's al - right now, In fact it's a gas...

But it's al - right, I'm Jum-pin' Jack Flash. It's a

King Of The Road.

Words and music by Roger Miller.

Moderately slow

1. Trail-er_____ for sale or rent;_____ Rooms_____ to let,
2. Third box_____ car, mid-night train;_____ Des-ti-na-tion
3. Trail-er_____ for sale or rent;_____ Rooms_____ to let,

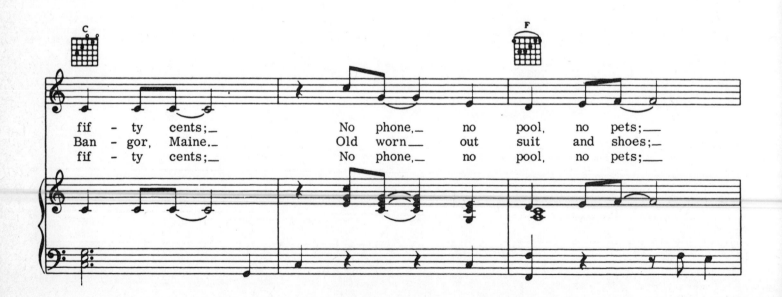

fif-ty cents;_____ No phone,_____ no pool, no pets;_____
Ban-gor, Maine._____ Old worn_____ out suit and shoes;_____
fif-ty cents;_____ No phone,_____ no pool, no pets;_____

145

D.S. al Fine 𝄋

The Last Thing On My Mind.

Words and music by Tom Paxton.

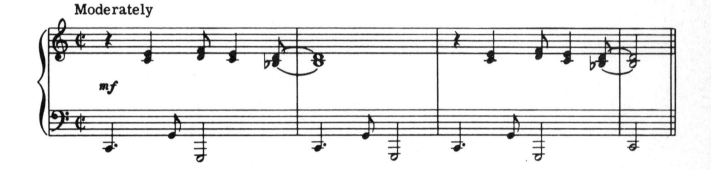

1. It's a les - son too late for the learn - ing _____ Made of

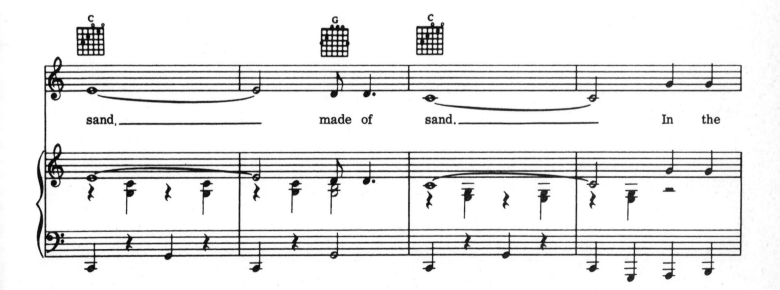

sand, _____ made of sand. _____ In the

2. As we walk, all my thoughts are a-tumblin',
'Round and 'round, 'round and 'round.
Underneath our feet the subway's rumblin',
Underground, underground.

(Chorus)

3. You've got reasons a-plenty for goin',
This I know, this I know.
For the weeds have been steadily growing,
Please don't go, please don't go.

(Chorus)

4. As I lie in my bed in the morning,
Without you, without you.
Each song in my breast dies a-borning,
Without you, without you.

(Chorus)

Leaving On A Jet Plane.

Words and music by John Denver.

1. All my bags are packed, I'm read-y to go, I'm
2. (There's so) man-y times I've let you down; So
3. (_____) Now the time has come to leave you,

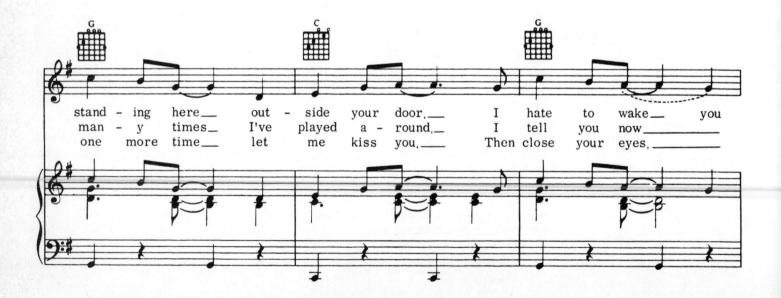

stand-ing here out-side your door, I hate to wake you
man-y times I've played a-round, I tell you now
one more time let me kiss you, Then close your eyes,

up to say_____ good - bye.   But the
they don't mean_____ a_____ thing.   Ev - 'ry
I'll be on_____ my_____ way.

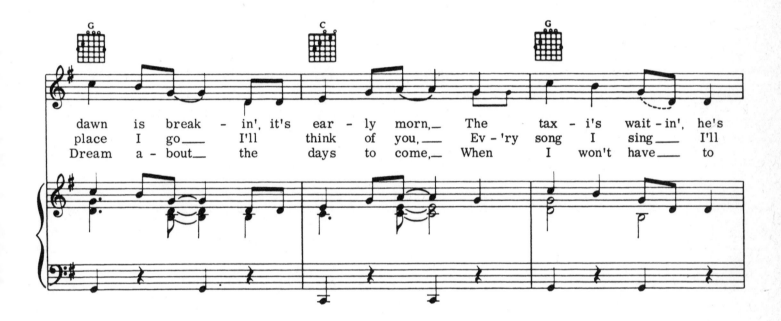

dawn is break - in', it's ear - ly morn,__ The tax - i's wait - in', he's
place I go__ I'll think of you,__ Ev - 'ry song I sing__ I'll
Dream a - bout__ the days to come,__ When I won't have__ to

blow - in' his horn.__ Al - read - y I'm so
sing for you.__ When I come back I'll
leave a - lone,__ A - bout the times_____

lone - some I ___ could ___ cry. ___
{bring / wear} your wed - ding ___ ring. ___
I won't have ___ to ___ say. ___

Chorus

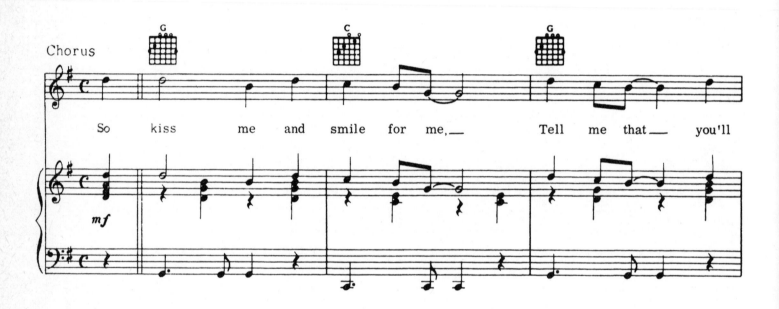

So kiss me and smile for me, ___ Tell me that ___ you'll

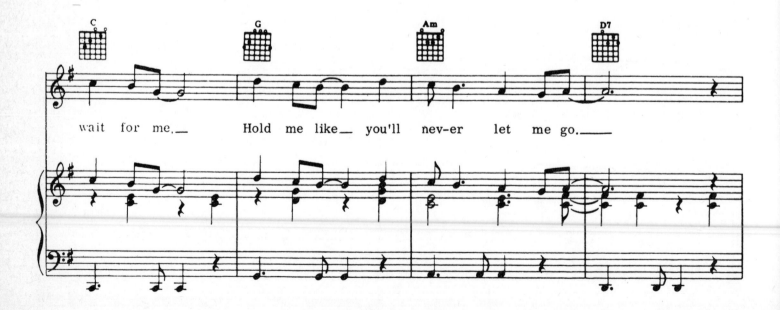

wait for me. ___ Hold me like ___ you'll nev-er let me go. ___

I'm Leav - in' On A Jet__ Plane, Don't know when

I'll be back__ a - gain. Oh babe,__ I hate __ to __

1.2. go. _____ 2. There's so

3. _____

go. _____ I'm

3. ———

Repeat and fade

Leav - in' On A Jet__ Plane, Don't know when I'll be back__ a - gain.

Repeat and fade

Let The Sunshine In.

Words by James Rado and Gerome Ragni.
Music by Galt MacDermot.

Moderately

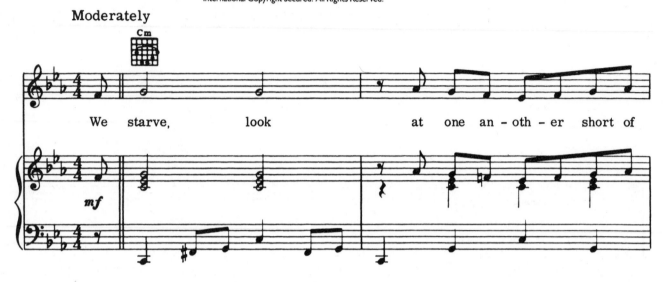

We starve, look   at one an-oth-er short of

breath,   walk — ing proud-ly in our win-ter

coats,   Wear — ing smells from lab-'ra-tor-ies,

fac - ing   a   dy - ing   na - tion_____ of   mov - ing   pa - per

fan - ta - sy,   Lis -t'ning for the new told lies   with su -

preme   vi - sions   of   lone - ly tunes.   Some   -   where,

in - side some - thing, there is a   rush   of   great -ness. Who knows what stands in

front   of   our lives; I fash-ion my___ fu - ture   on

films in space.   Si - lence tells   me   se - cret - ly

ev -   'ry - thing,___   ev -   'ry - thing.___

___   Sing   -   ing   my space songs on a spi-der-

web si - tar, "Life is a - round_ you and in you."

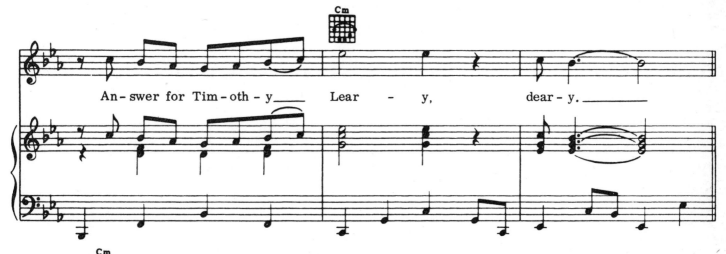

An - swer for Tim - oth - y____ Lear - y, dear - y.____

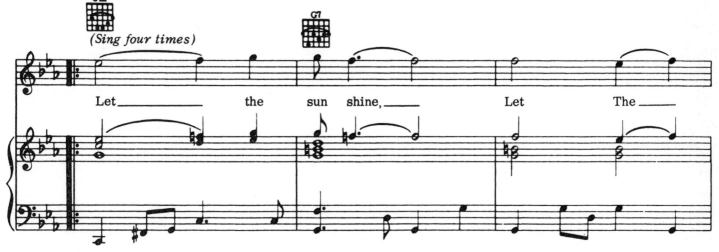

(Sing four times)

Let_____ the sun shine,____ Let The____

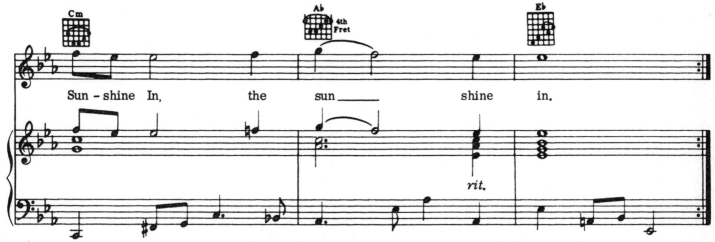

Sun - shine In, the sun_____ shine in.

rit.

Somethin' Stupid.

Words and Music by C. Carson Parks.

Moderately Slow

I know I stand in line un-til you think you have the time to spend an eve-nin' with me._____

prac-tice ev-'ry day to find some clev-er lines to say to make the mean-ing come through._____

And if we go some place to dance, I know that there's a chance you won't be

But then I think I'll wait un-til the eve-nin' gets late and I'm a-

leav-in' with me._____ Then af-ter-wards we drop in - to a

lone with you._____ The time is right, your per-fume fills my

Love Me With All Your Heart.

English lyric by Michael Vaughn. Original words by Marie Rigual.
Music by Carlos Rigual.

Moderately slow with a strong beat

Love me with all your heart, that's all I want, love; _____

Love me with all of your heart, or not at all;

161

Don't give me your love ___ for a mo-ment ___ or an hou-r, ___ Love me

al-ways ___ as you loved me ___ from the start, With ev'-ry beat of your heart. ___

heart. _____

Massachusetts.

Words and music by Barry, Robin and Maurice Gibb.

Copyright © 1967 by Abigail Music (Australia) Pty. Ltd., for Australasia, Japan and South Africa
Copyright © 1967 by Abigail Music (London) Ltd., 67 Brook Street, London W1 for the rest of the World.
International Copyright Secured. All Rights Reserved.

Moderato

Feel   I'm go-in'   back _____   to Mass - a -
Tried   to hitch a   ride _____   to San   Fran-
Talk   a-bout the   life _____   in Mass - a

chu - setts,   Some - thing's tell - ing   me _____
cis - co,   Got -   ta   do   the   things _____
chu - setts,   Speak   a - bout the   peo -

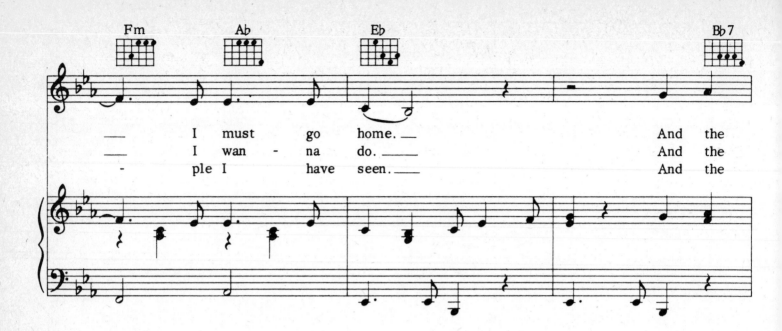

I must go home. ____ And the
I wan - na do. ____ And the
- ple I have seen. ____ And the

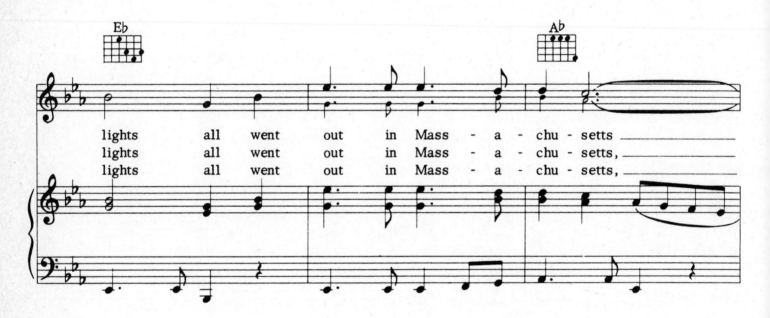

lights all went out in Mass - a - chu - setts ____
lights all went out in Mass - a - chu - setts, ____
lights all went out in Mass - a - chu - setts, ____

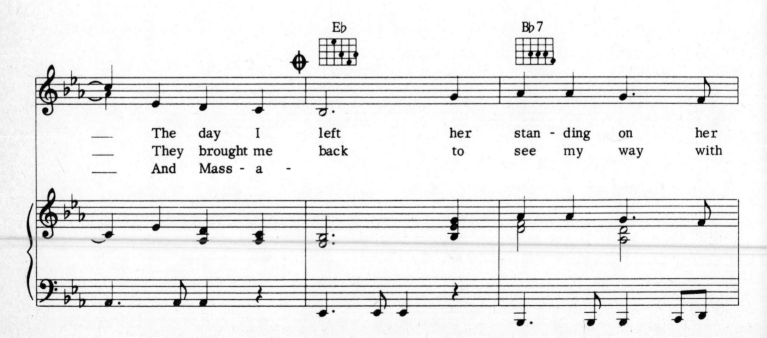

____ The day I left her stan - ding on her
____ They brought me back to see my way with
____ And Mass - a -

Coda

Mich - elle, ma belle, Sont les mots qui vont très bien en -

semble, très bien en - semble; I will say the on - ly words I know that

you'll un - der - stand, My Mich - elle.

repeat and fade

169

Milord.

Original lyrics by G. Moustaki.
Music by Marguerite Monnot. Words by Bunny Lewis.

Foxtrot tempo

Come on, get

Chorus

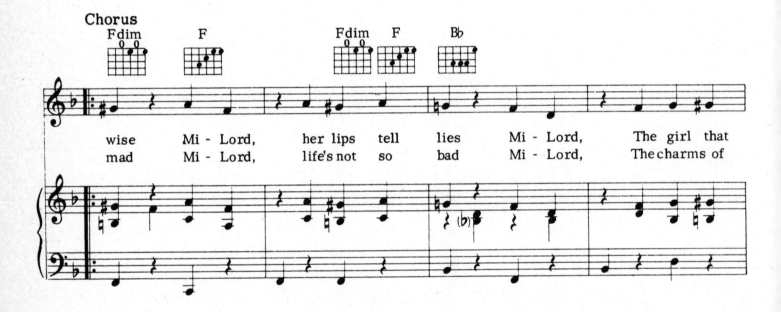

wise   Mi - Lord,   her lips   tell   lies   Mi - Lord,   The girl that
mad   Mi - Lord,   life's not   so   bad   Mi - Lord,   The charms of

you   a - dored has   found some o - ther   guy. She just got
o - ther   arms   can   make your heart for - get. Don't count the

bored   Mi - Lord,   Now you're ig - nored   Mi - Lord,   Deep down in -
cost   Mi - Lord,   Let her get   lost   Mi - Lord,   One mem-o -

side   your pride   won't   let you   say "Good - bye."   That South - ern
ry   can be   a   life - time of re - gret.   So let her

Belle   Mi - Lord,   has got   a   heart   of ice,   Love can be
go   Mi - Lord,   come on, re - lax   be smart,   'Cos if you

171

hell Mi - Lord, as well as Pa - ra - dise. You
don't you know as she'll on - ly break your heart. The

Verse

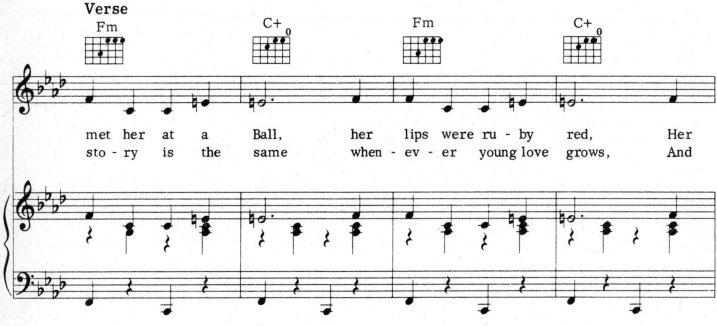

met her at a Ball, her lips were ru - by red, Her
sto - ry is the same when - ev - er young love grows, And

la - zy South-ern drawl soon turn'd your no - ble head. You
no - one is to blame, it's just the way it goes, You're

swore you'd nev - er part, tho' you lived far a - way, How
not the first who's found that love can be un - kind, And

could you know her heart, Like o - ther hearts, would stray. _____ Come on, get
still the world goes round, But one heart's left be - hind. _____ Come on, get

Hip, Mi-Lord, and let life rip Mi-Lord, Be sure there's plen-ty more of

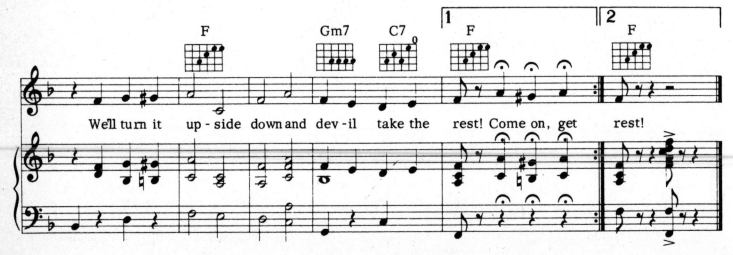

Mr Tambourine Man.

Words and music by Bob Dylan.

Hey! Mis-ter Tam-bou-rine Man play a song for me, I'm not

sleep-y and there is no place I'm go-in' to. _____

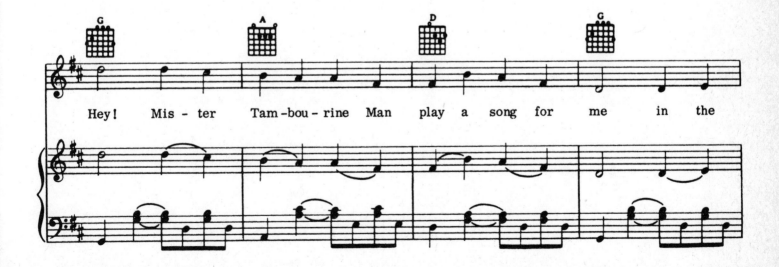

Hey! Mis-ter Tam-bou-rine Man play a song for me in the

5th time Fine

jin-gle jan-gle morn-in' I'll come fol – low-in' you.

Verse

1. Though I know that eve-nin's em-pire has re-turned in-to sand,

Van-ished from my hand, Left me blind-ly here to stand but still not

sleep-in'! My wea-ri-ness a – maz-es me I'm

Repeat 3 times

brand - ed on my feet. I have no one to meet And the

an - cient emp - ty street's too dead for dream - in'._____

(Chorus)

2. Take me on a trip upon your magic swirlin' ship
   My senses have been stripped, my hands can't feel to grip
   My toes too numb to step, wait only for my boot heels
   To be wanderin'
   I'm ready to go anywhere, I'm ready for to fade
   Into my own parade, cast your dancin' spell my way
   I promise to go under it.

   (Chorus)

3. Though you might hear laughin' spinnin' swingin' madly across the sun
   It's not aimed at anyone, it's just escapin' on the run
   And but for the sky there are no fences facin'
   And if you hear vague traces of skippin' reels of rhyme
   To your tambourine in time, it's just a ragged clown behind
   I wouldn't pay it any mind, it's just a shadow you're
   Seein' that he's chasin'.

   (Chorus)

4. Then take me disappearin' through the smoke rings of my mind
   Down the foggy ruins of time, far past the frozen leaves
   The haunted, frightened trees out to the windy beach
   Far from the twisted reach of crazy sorrow
   Yes, to dance beneath the diamond sky with one hand wavin' free
   Silhouetted by the sea, circled by the circus sands
   With all memory and fate driven deep beneath the waves
   Let me forget about today until tomorrow.

   (Chorus)

My Way.

French lyric by Gilles Thibaut. English lyric by Paul Anka.
Music by Claude Francois and Jacques Revaux.

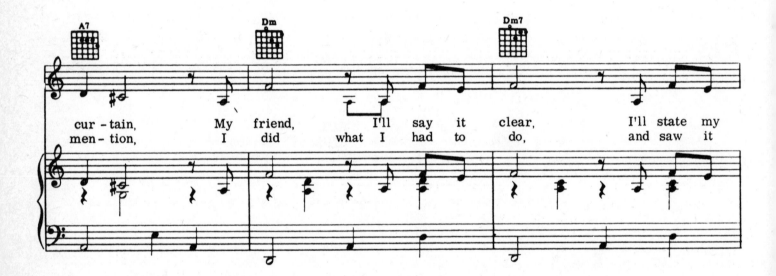

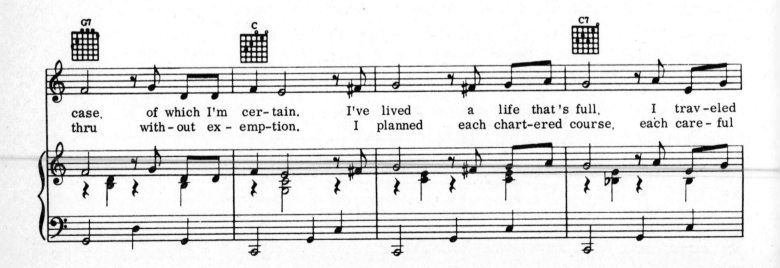

each and ev-'ry high-way, And more, much more than this, I did it
step a-long the by-way, And more, much more than this, I did it

1. My Way. Re-
2. My Way. Yes, there were

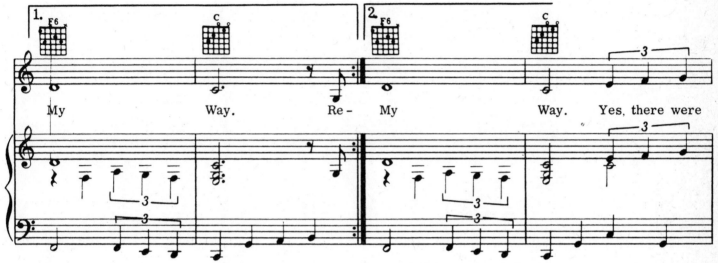

times, I'm sure you knew, when I bit off more than I could chew, But thru it

all, when there was doubt, I ate it up, and spit it out. I faced it

Never On Sunday.

Lyric by Billy Towne.
Music by Manos Hadjidakis.

Moderately

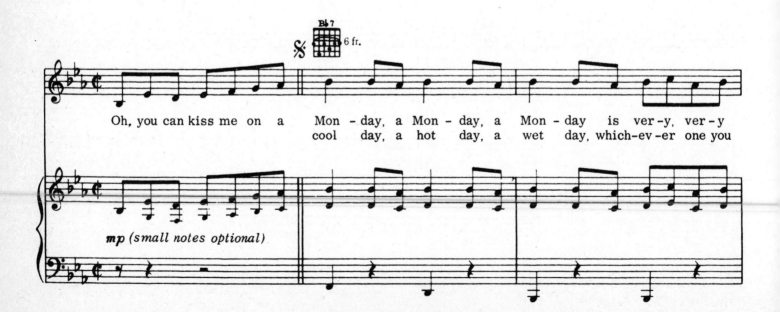

Oh, you can kiss me on a Mon-day, a Mon-day, a Mon-day is ver-y, ver-y
cool day, a hot day, a wet day, which-ev-er one you

mp (small notes optional)

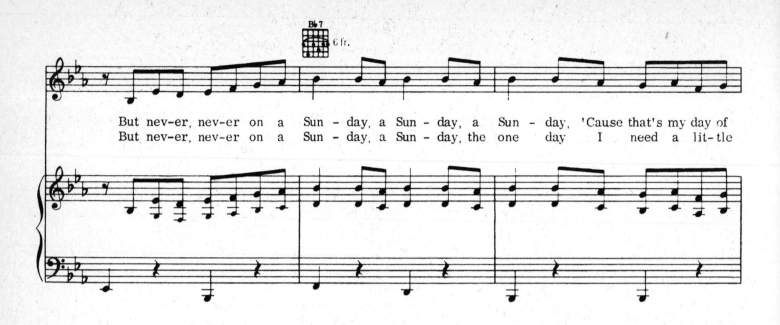

But nev-er, nev-er on a Sun-day, a Sun-day, a Sun-day, 'Cause that's my day of
But nev-er, nev-er on a Sun-day, a Sun-day, the one day I need a lit-tle

1. rest. Most an - y rest.

2. *Fine*

day_____ you can be my guest,_____ An - y day you

No Regrets.

French lyric by Michel Vaucaire. English lyric by Irving Taylor.
Music by Charles Dumont.

Slowly

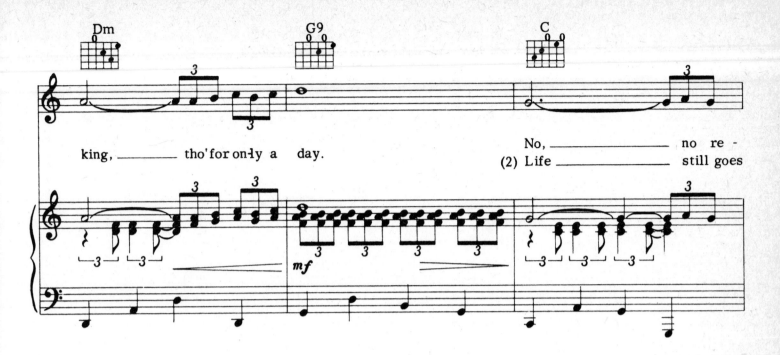

king, _____ tho'for on-ly a day.   No, _____ no re-
(2) Life _____ still goes

grets,   No, _____ let there be no re-grets, _____ Why ex-
on,   Yes, _____ ev-en tho' love is gone, _____ One last

plain, _____ why de - lay?   Don't go a - way, _____ simply call it a
kiss, _____ shrug and sigh, _____ No re-

day. _____ Plea-ding mo-ments we knew, _____ I will set them a - part, _____ Ev-'ry look, ev-'ry

sigh _____ will be burn'd in my heart, _____ But no tear will be shed, _____ There'll be no-one to

blame, _____ Let it al-ways be said _____ we at-temp-ted what came.

D.S. al

Coda

grets _____ as we whis-per good - bye. _____

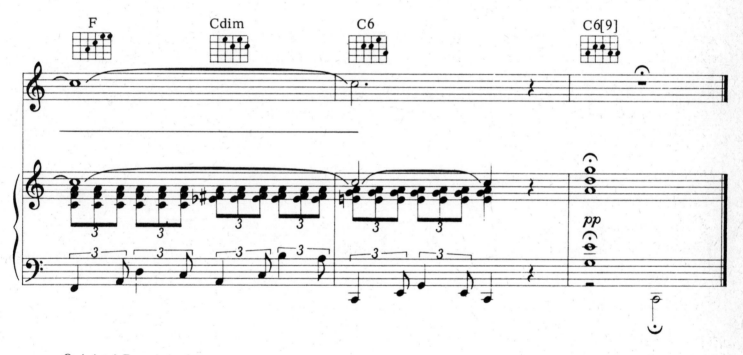

Original French lyrics

1 Non! Rien de rien, Non! Je ne regrette rien,
  Ni le bien, qu'on m'a fait,
  Ni le mal, tout ça m'est bien égal!
  Non! Rien de rien, Non! Je ne regrette rien,
  C'est payé, balayé,
  Oublié, je me fous du passé!

2 Non! Rien de rien, Non! Je ne regrette rien,
  Ni le bien, qu'on m'a fait,
  Ni le mal, tout ça m'est bien égal!
  Non! Rien de rien, Non! Je ne regrette rien,
  Car ma vie, car me joies,
  Aujourd'hui, ça commence avec toi!

Interlude   Avec mes souvenirs, j'ai allumé le feu,
Mes chagrins, mes plaisirs, je n'ai plus besoin d'eux!
Balayés les amours, et tous leurs trémolos,
Balayés pour toujours, je repars à zéro.

Ob-La-Di, Ob-La-Da.

Words and music by John Lennon and Paul McCartney.

Bright tempo

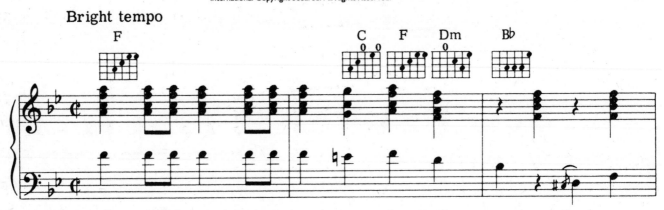

Des-mond has a bar-row in the mar-ket place,___ Mol-ly is the

sing-er in a band.   Des - mond says to Mol-ly, "Girl, I

like your face,"__ And Mol-ly says this as she takes him by the hand,__

Ob - la - di __ ob - la - da,__ Life goes on, __ Bra - la -

-la, How the life goes on.___ Ob-la-di___ob-la da___

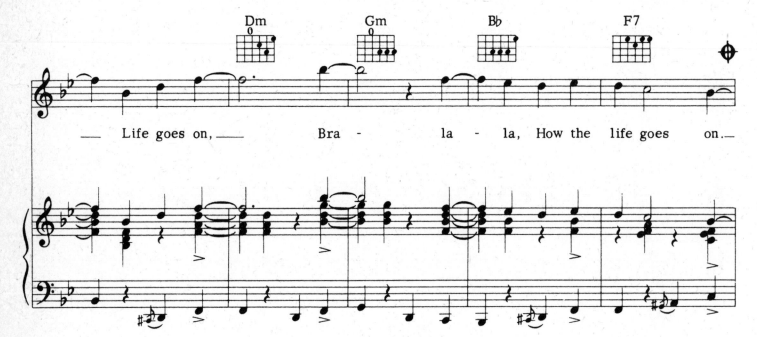

Bb   Dm   Gm   Bb   F7

___ Life goes on,___ Bra-___ la-la, How the life goes on.___

Bb   1   2   Eb

___   In a cou-ple of

years they have built a home__ sweet home.__

With a cou-ple of kids run-ning in the yard__

__ Of Des-mond and Mol _ ly Jones. __

D.S. al ⊕ %
(twice)

And if you want some fun __

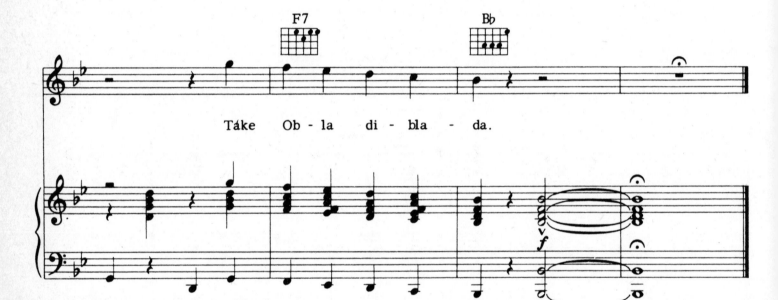

Táke Ob - la - di - bla - da.

2 Desmond takes a trolley to the jeweller's stores,
   Buys a twenty carat golden ring,
   Takes it back to Molly waiting at the door,
   And as he gives it to her she begins to sing,

3 Happy ever after in the market place
   Desmond lets the children lend a hand;
   Molly stays at home and does her pretty face,
   And in the evening she still sings it with the band.

4 Happy ever after in the market place
   Molly lets the children lend a hand;
   Desmond stays at home and does his pretty face,
   And in the evening she's a singer with the band.

Penny Lane.

Words and music by John Lennon and Paul McCartney.

Moderate tempo

In Pen-ny Lane ___ there is a bar - ber show-ing pho -
cor - ner is a bank - er with a mo -
the bar-ber shaves ___ an - oth - er cus -

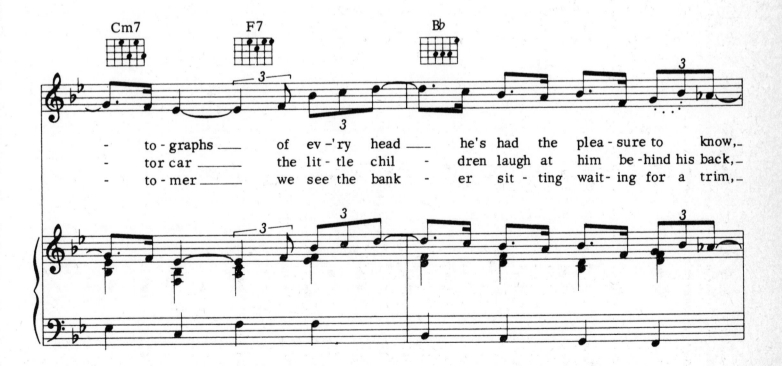

- to - graphs ___ of ev -'ry head ___ he's had the plea-sure to know, __
- tor car ___ the lit - tle chil - dren laugh at him be -hind his back, __
- to - mer ___ we see the bank - er sit - ting wait-ing for a trim, __

And all the peo-ple that come and go ___ stop and say ___
And the bank-er nev-er wears a mack in the pour -
And then the fire - man rush-es in ___ from the pour -

___ "hel-lo."
- ing rain.
- ing rain.

On the

Ve-ry strange ___ Pen-ny Lane ___

___ is in my ears ___ and in my eyes. ___

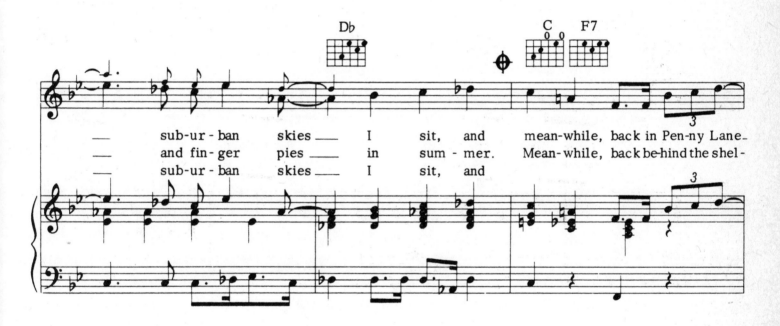

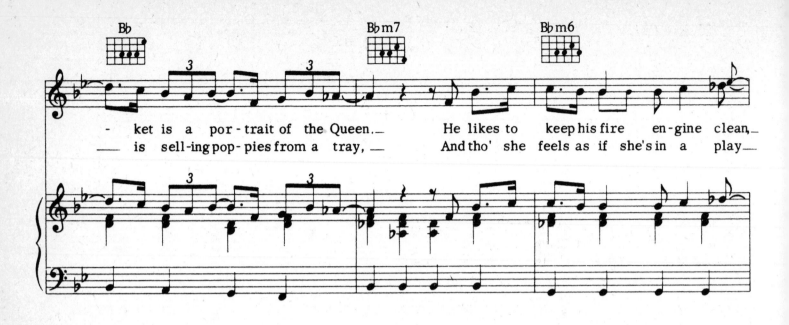

ket is a por-trait of the Queen.___ He likes to keep his fire en-gine clean,
___ is sell-ing pop-pies from a tray,___ And tho' she feels as if she's in a play

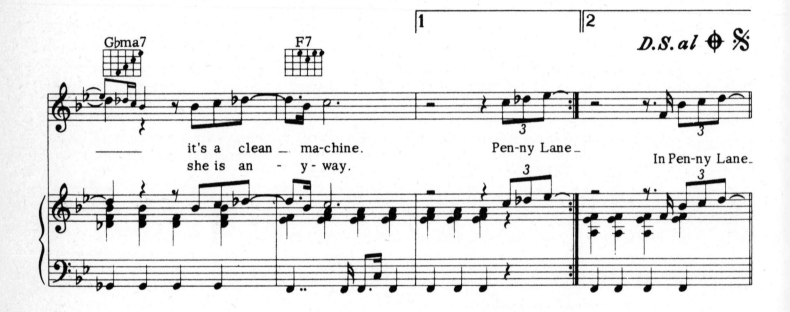

it's a clean ___ ma-chine.
she is an ___ y-way.

1 Pen-ny Lane___

2 In Pen-ny Lane___

D.S. al ⊕ 𝄋

⊕ *Coda*

F7   Bb

mean-while back Pen-ny Lane ___ is in my ears ___ and in my eyes.___

There be-neath the blue___ sub-ur-ban skies___

Pen-ny Lane.___

Proud Mary.

Words and music by J. C. Fogerty.

Moderately, with a heavy beat

Verse
G

Left a good job — in the ci - ty, —
Cleaned a lot of plates in Mem - phis,

Work - in' for The Man ev'ry night and day, — And I ne - ver lost one min -
Pumped a lot of pain in New Or - leans, — But I ne - ver saw the good -

- ute of sleep - in', Wor-ry-in''bout the way things might have been._
___ side of the ci-ty Un - til I hitched a ride on a riv - er boat queen._

Chorus

Big wheel_ keep on _ turn-in', _ Proud Ma-ry keep on burn - in', _ Roll-

- in', _ roll - in', _ roll - in' on the riv - er. ___

Verse

If you come down to the riv-er, Bet you gon-na find some peo - ple who live.

D.S. al ⊕ ⅀

You don't have to wor-ry 'cause you have no mon-ey, Peo-ple on the riv-er are hap-py to give.

⊕ *Coda*

repeat and fade

Roll-in', roll - in', roll-in' on the riv - er.

Respect.

Words and music by Otis Redding, Jr.

my   pro-per res - pect   when you get   home.   Yeah,
is   give me some here   when you get   home.   Yeah,

ba – by,   when   you get   home.
ba – by,   when   you get   home.

R – E – S – P – E – C – T,   find out what·it means to me,   R – E – S – P – E – C – T,

Repeat and fade out

take out   T – C – P,   a lit-tle re - pect.

Release Me.

Words and music by Eddie Miller, Dub Williams, Robert Yount and Robert Harris.

Moderato, with feeling

Please re - lease me, let me go _____ For
I have found a new love, dear, _____ And
Please re - lease me, can't you see _____ You'd

I don't love you an - y - more. To
I will al - ways want her near. Her
be a fool to cling to me. To

waste our lives would be a sin. _____ Re -
lips are warm while yours are cold. _____ Re -
live a lie would bring us pain, _____ So re-

lease me and let me love a - gain.
lease me, my dar - ling, let me go.
lease me and let me love a -

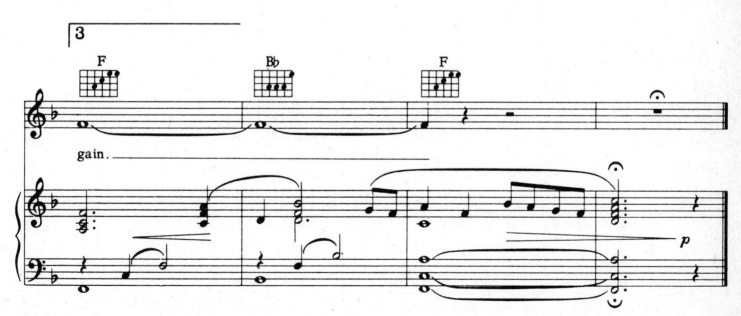

gain. _____

River Deep – Mountain High.

Words and music by Phil Spector, Ellie Greenwich and Jeff Barry.

Moderato, with a strong beat

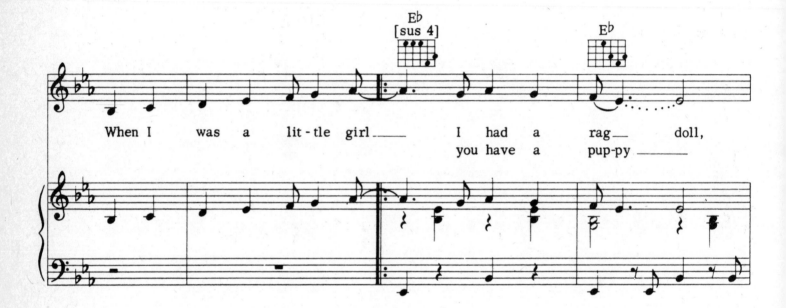

When I was a lit-tle girl___ I had a rag___ doll,
you have a pup-py _____

The on-ly doll ___ I've ev-er owned. ___
That al-ways fol - lowed you a - round? ___

er,___   let me say,___   And it gets high-

ger, ba - by,   and hea-ven knows,___   And it gets sweet-

er___   day by day.___

er, ba - by,   as it grows.___

Chorus

Do I   love you,   right or wrong?_____   Yeah

river — deep, moun-tain high, — yeah yeah yeah. —

If I lost you, would I cry? —

fine

I would, ba - by, — ba - by, — ba - by. —

When you were a young boy did—

a tempo

2

Bb

I love you, ba - by, like a flow - er loves the spring, ____

And I ___ love you, ba - by, like a ro - bin loves to sing, ____

Eb

And I love you, ba - by, like_a school-boy loves a pra - nk, ____

Bb

D.S. al fine

And I love you, ba - by, riv-er deep,___ moun-tain high. ____

212

Spanish Eyes.

Lyric by Charles Singleton and Eddie Snyder.
Music by Bert Kaempfert.

Moderato

Blue _____ Span-ish eyes, _____
Blue _____ Span-ish eyes, _____

Tear-drops are fall - ing from your Span-ish eyes. _____
Pret-ti - est eyes in all of Mex-i - co. _____

Please,_____ please don't cry,_____
True _____ Span - ish eyes,_____

This is just a - dios and not good - bye._____
Please smile for me once more be - fore I go._____

Soon _____ I'll re - turn _____

215

Satisfaction (I Can't Get No).

Words and music by Mick Jagger and Keith Richard.

try   and I try   and I try   and I try.___   I can't

get   no...   I   can't   get   no...

1. When I'm
2. When I'm
3. When I'm

driv - in' in my car,___   And that   man comes on the ra - di - o; And he's
watch - in' my T. V.,___   And that   man comes on to tell___ me;___ How___
rid - in' 'round the world,___   And I'm   do - in' this and I'm sign-in' that; And I'm

tell-in' me more and more__ a-bout some use - less in - for-ma-tion, Sup-posed to__
white__ my shirts can be,____ Well, he can't be a man, 'cause he__ does-n't smoke the__
try-in' to make some girl._Who tells me, "Ba-by, bet-ter come back lat - er next week, 'cause you

fire__ my im-ag - i-na - tion,
same cig-a-rettes as me.____ I can't get no, Oh, no, no,
see I'm on a los-ing streak."____

no, Hey, hey, hey__ that's what I say.__

I can't get no, I can't

get no, I Can't Get No Sat-is-

fac-tion, No Sat-is - fac-tion, No Sat-is -

fac-tion, No Sat-is - fac-tion.

fade out

She Loves You.

Words and music by John Lennon and Paul McCartney.

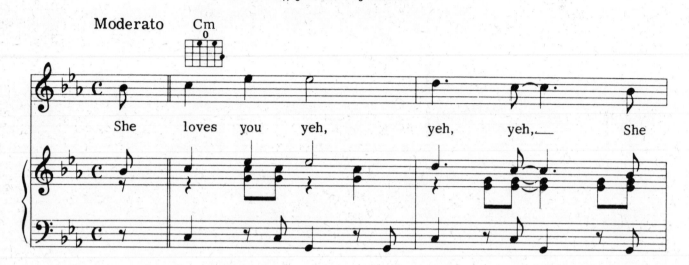

She loves you yeh, yeh, yeh,___ She

loves you yeh, yeh, yeh,___ She loves you yeh,

yeh, yeh, yeh!!! _____ 1 You

think you've lost your love, ____   Well I saw her yes - ter - day-yi-yay,   It's
said you hurt her so ____   She al - most lost her mind, ____   And
know it's up to you, ____   I think it's on - ly fair, ____

you she's think- ing of, ____   And she told me what to say-yi-ay. She says she
now she says she knows ____   You're not the hurt - ing kind. ____ She says she
Pride can hurt you too, ____   A - pol-o - gize to her ____ Be-cause she

loves you,   and you know that can't be bad, _____ Yes, she

loves you, and you know you should be glad. ___ 2 She

Oo She loves you yeh, yeh, yeh, ___ She loves you yeh,

yeh, yeh, ___ And with a love like that you know you should be glad. ___

3 You

With a love like that you

know you should ___ be glad, _____

Yeh,

rit.   *a tempo*

yeh, yeh, ___   yeh,   yeh, yeh, ___   yeh. _____

Something Is Happening.

English lyric by Jack Fishman.
Music by R. Del Turco and G. Bigazzi.

Brightly

Some - thing is hap-pen - ing, and it star-ted hap-pen - ing when
Some - thing is hap-pen - ing, ex - ci - ting, be - wil - der-ing, you
You do do do do do do do do do do do do do

you walked by - yi - yi. _____ Some - thing is hap-pen - ing, and
must know why-yi - yi. _____ Some - thing is hap-pen - ing, I
do yi - yi-yi - yi. _____ Do do do do do do do

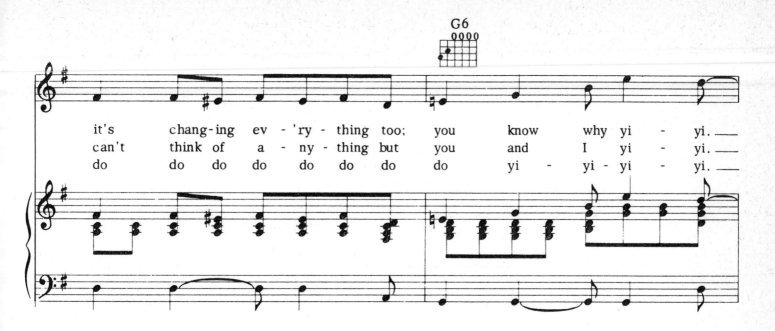

it's   chang-ing   ev - 'ry - thing too;   you   know   why yi -   yi. _____
can't   think   of   a - ny - thing but   you   and   I   yi -   yi. _____
do   do   do   do   do   do   do   do   yi -   yi - yi -   yi. _____

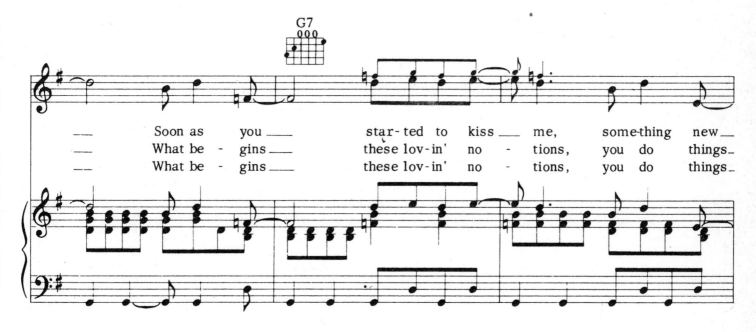

_____ Soon as   you _____   star - ted to kiss _____ me,   some-thing new _____
_____ What be - gins _____   these lov-in' no - tions,   you do things_
_____ What be - gins _____   these lov-in' no - tions,   you do things_

_____ sud - den - ly hit _____ me.   The   world   o - ver
_____ to my e - mo - tions.   I   can't   help   what -
_____ to my e - mo - tions.   I   can't   help   what -

225

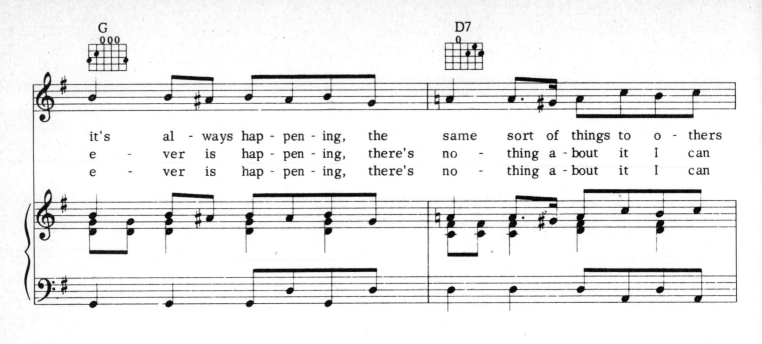

it's   al - ways hap - pen - ing,   the   same   sort of things to o - thers
e - ver is hap - pen - ing,   there's   no - thing a - bout it   I   can
e - ver is hap - pen - ing,   there's   no - thing a - bout it   I   can

too.
do.   Some - thing is hap-pen-ing to   me,   and I on - ly hope the
do.

same   thing is hap - pen - ing to   you.

same thing is hap-pen-ing to same thing is hap-pen-ing to

you.
do da do da do da da ___ da da

do da do da do da da ___ da da do da do da

Spinning Wheel.

Words and music by David Clayton Thomas.

Moderately slow, with a beat

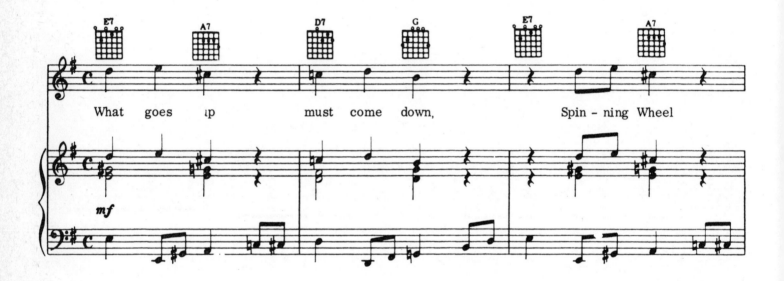

What goes up must come down, Spin-ning Wheel

got to go 'round.__ Talk-in' 'bout your trou-bles, it's a cry-in' sin,__

Did you find your di-rect-ing sign__ on the straight and nar-row high-

-way.__ Would you mind__ a re-flect-ing sign?__ Just

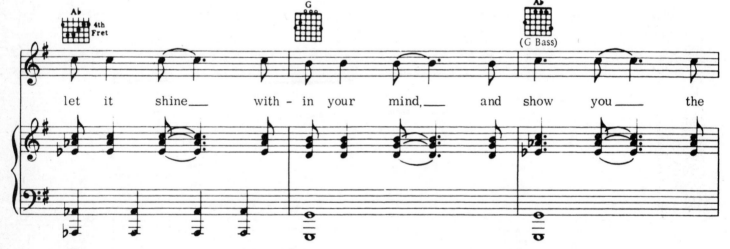

let it shine__ with-in your mind,__ and show you__ the

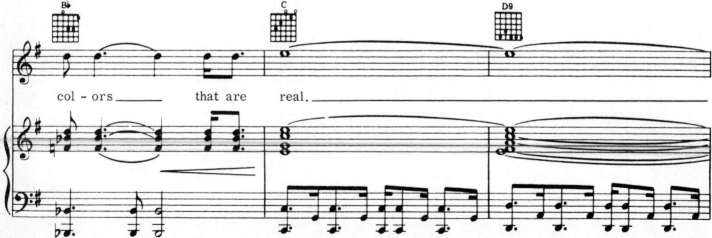

col-ors__ that are real.__

Some-one is wait-ing just for you,___

Spin-ning Wheel spin-ning true,___ Drop all your trou-bles by the

riv - er side,___ Catch a paint - ed po - ny on the

Tacet

Spin-ning Wheel__ ride.

Repeat and fade

Sugar, Sugar.

Words and music by Jeff Barry and Andy Kim.

Moderately

Su - gar, ah, hon-ey, hon-ey, You are my

can - dy girl,_ And you've got me want-ing you._

Hon-ey, ah, — Su-gar, Su-gar, You are my

can - dy girl, — And you've got me want-ing you. —

I just can't be - lieve the love - li - ness of lov - ing you.
When I kissed you, girl, I knew how sweet a kiss could be. (I

Spanish Harlem.

Words and music by Jerry Leiber and Phil Spector.

Baion moderato

There is a rose in Span-ish Har-lem,_____

A rare rose up in Span-ish Har-lem,_____

It is a spe-cial one,— it's nev-er seen the sun,— It on-ly
With eyes as black as coal— that look down in my soul— And start a

comes up when the moon is on the run and all the stars are glea-ming,—
fire— there and then I lose con-trol, I have to beg your par-don,—

It's grow-ing in the street right up thro' the con-crete, But

237

soft and sound— in pale moon.

I'm going to pick that rose— and watch her as she grows ———— in my

gar-den. ————————

There Goes My Everything.

Words and music by Dallas Frazier.

Moderately slow

Verse

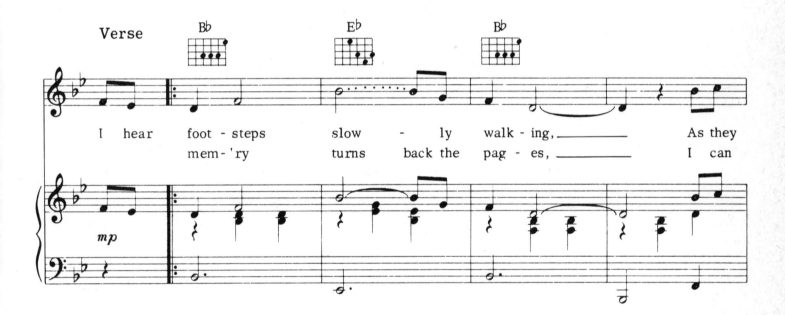

I hear foot-steps slow-ly walk-ing, _____ As they
mem-'ry turns back the pag-es, _____ I can

gent-ly walk a-cross _____ a lone-ly floor. _____ And a
see the hap-py years _____ we had be-fore. _____ Now the

voice ___ is soft - ly say - ing, _____ "Dar-ling,
love ___ that kept this old heart beat - ing _____ Has been

this will be good - bye ___ for ev - er - more." _____
shat-tered by the clos - ing of the door. _____

Chorus

There goes my rea - son for liv - ing,

There goes the one of my dreams, _____

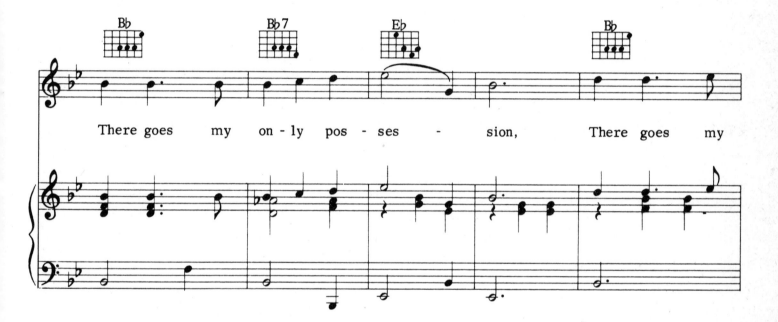

There goes my on - ly pos - ses - sion, There goes my

ev - 'ry - thing. 2 As my thing. _____

rit.

mp

Big Spender.

Words by Dorothy Fields.
Music by Cy Coleman.

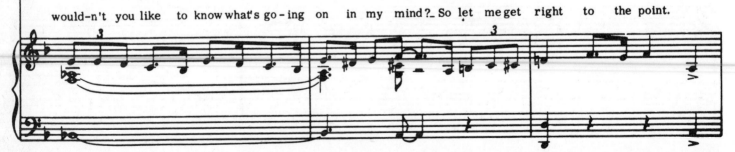

I don't pop my cork for ev' - ry guy I see.

Hey! Big Spen - der, Spend a lit -tle time with

me. Would-n't you like to have

fun, fun, fun? How's a-bout a few laughs, laughs? I can show you a

Those Were The Days.

Words and music by Gene Raskin.

Chorus

hours,   And dreamed of   all   the great things we would do.   Those Were The
tav-ern, We'd smile   at   one an-oth-er and we'd say   Those Were The
flec-tion. Was that lone-ly fel-low real-ly me?   Those Were The
wis-er.   For   in   our hearts the dreams are still the same.   Those Were The

A Tempo

Days,   my friend.__ We thought they'd nev-er end,__ We'd sing and dance   for-

ev-er and a day;   We'd live the life   we chose,__ We'd fight and

246

nev - er lose,___ For we were young and sure___ to have our

way. La la la la la la___ la la la

la la la___ Those Were The Days, Oh yes, Those Were The

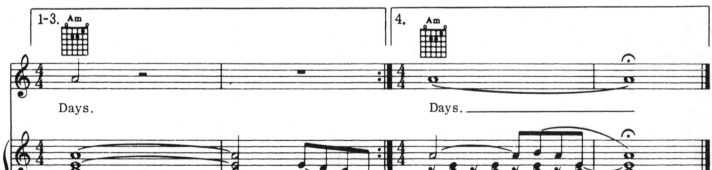

Days. Days.___

Trains And Boats And Planes.

Music by Burt Bacharach.
Words by Hal David.

Moderately

Trains and boats and planes ___ are pass-ing by, ___ They mean a trip
We were so in love, ___ and high a - bove ___ We had a star

___ to Pa - ris or Rome ___ to some-one else, ___ but not for me.
___ to wish ___ up - on, wish ___ and dreams come true, ___ but not for me.

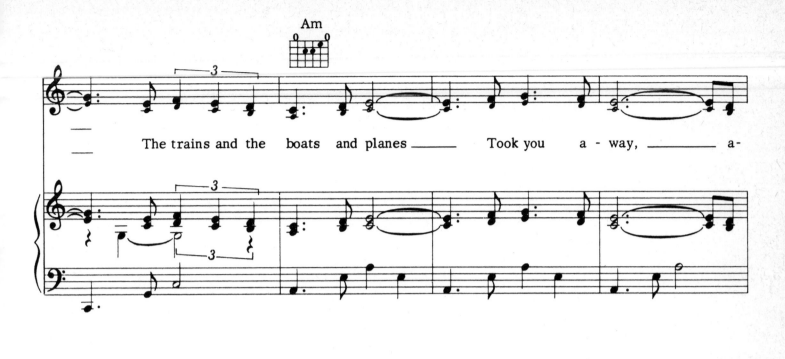

The trains and the boats and planes _____ Took you a - way, _____ a-

way from me. _____ — You are from an -

o - ther part _ of the world, _____ You had to go _ back a - while, and then

And if my prayer ___ can cross the sea, ___ The trains and the

boats and planes ___ Will bring you back, ___ back home to me. ___

Turn! Turn! Turn!

Words: Book of Ecclesiastes Adaptation and music by Peter Seeger.

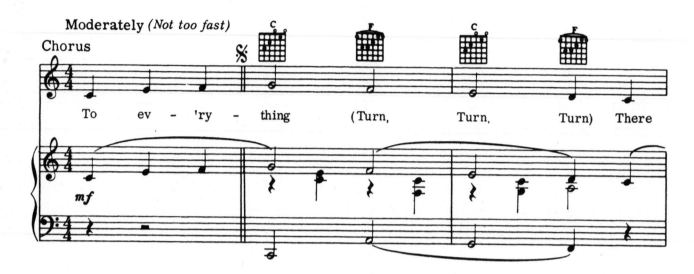

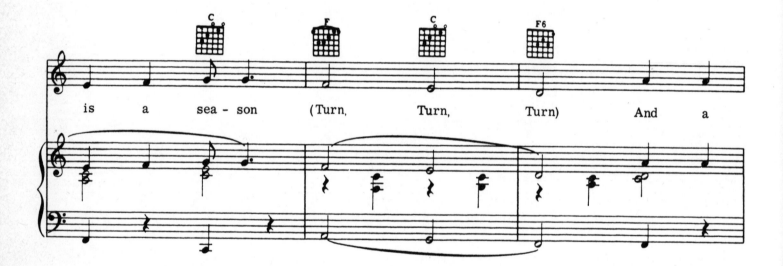

Verse

2. A time to build up, a time to break down;
   A time to dance, a time to mourn;
   A time to cast away stones,
   A time to gather stones together.

3. A time of love, a time of hate;
   A time of war, a time of peace;
   A time you may embrace,
   A time to refrain from embracing.

4. A time to gain, a time to lose;
   A time to rend, a time to sew;
   A time to love, a time to hate;
   A time for peace, I swear it's not too late.

The Times They Are A-Changin'.

Words and music by Bob Dylan.

Moderately

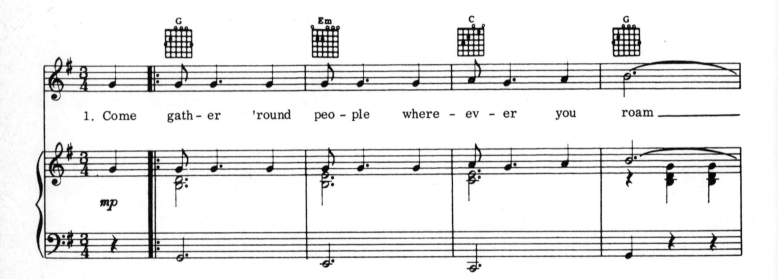

1. Come gath-er 'round peo-ple where-ev-er you roam

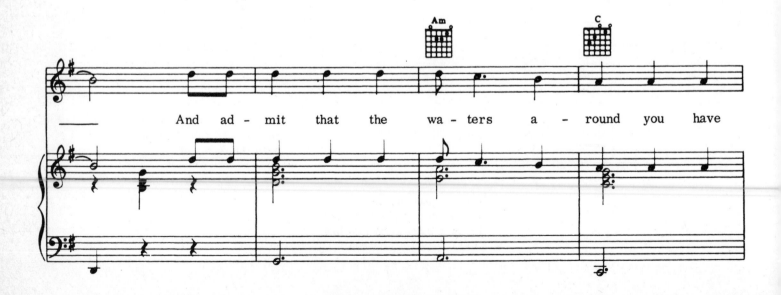

And ad-mit that the wa-ters a-round you have

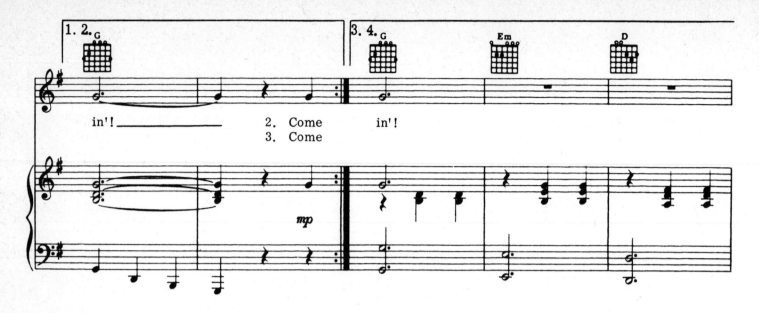

in'! _____ 2. Come in'!
3. Come

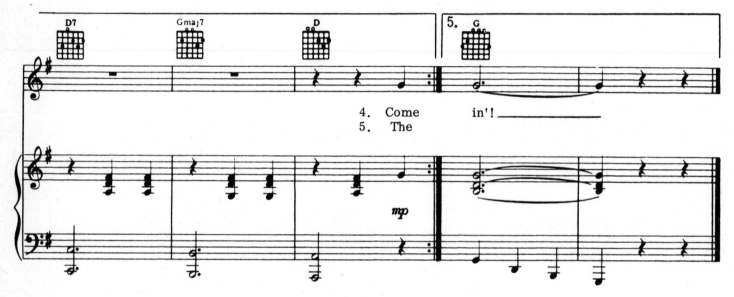

4. Come in'! _____
5. The

2. Come writers and critics
   Who prophesies with your pen
   And keep your eyes wide
   The chance won't come again.
   And don't speak too soon
   For the wheel's still in spin
   And there's no tellin' who
   That it's namin'
   For the loser now
   Will be later to win
   For the times they are a-changin'.

3. Come senators. congressmen
   Please heed the call
   Don't stand in the doorway
   Don't block up the hall.
   For he that gets hurt
   Will be he who has stalled
   There's a battle
   Outside and it's ragin'
   It'll soon shake your windows
   And rattle your walls
   For the times they are a-changin'.

4. Come mothers and fathers,
   Throughout the land
   And don't criticize
   What you can't understand.
   Your sons and your daughters
   Are beyond your command
   Your old road is
   Rapidly agin'
   Please get out of the new one
   If you can't lend your hand
   For the times they are a-changin'.

5. The line it is drawn
   The curse it is cast
   The slow one now will
   Later be fast.
   As the present now
   Will later be past
   The order is rapidly fadin'
   And the first one now
   Will later be last
   For the times they are a-changin'.

Walk On By.

Words by Hal David.
Music by Burt Bacharach.

With a beat

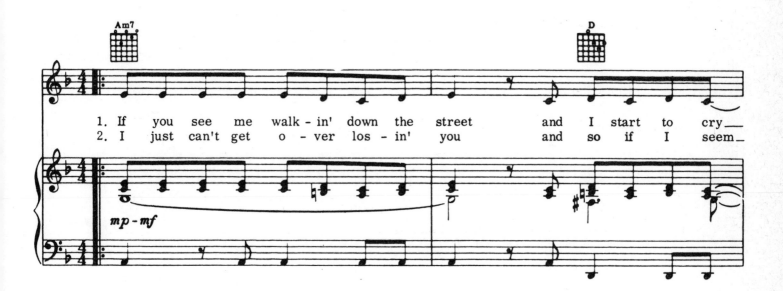

1. If you see me walk - in' down the street and I start to cry___
2. I just can't get o - ver los - in' you and so if I seem___

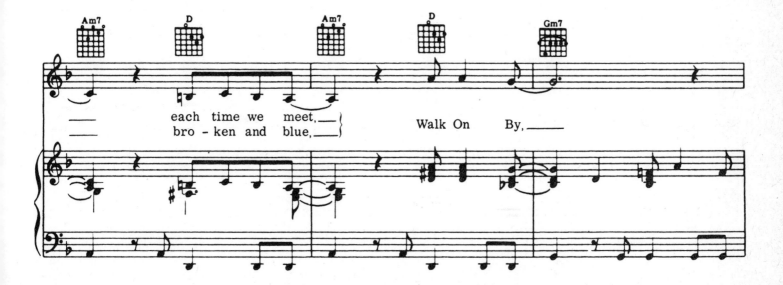

___ each time we meet,___ }
___ bro - ken and blue,___ } Walk On By,___

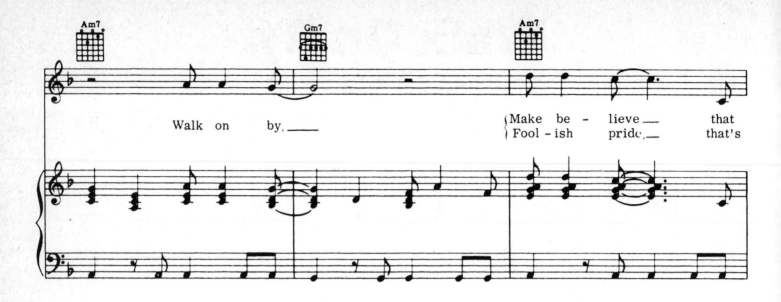

Walk on by, ____

Make be - lieve ____ that
Fool - ish pride, ____ that's

you don't see the tears, Just let me grieve ____ in
all that I have left, So let me hide ____ in the

pri - vate, 'Cause each time I see you, I break down and
tears and the sad - ness you gave me when you said good-

cry.}
bye.}
Walk on by,___ Don't

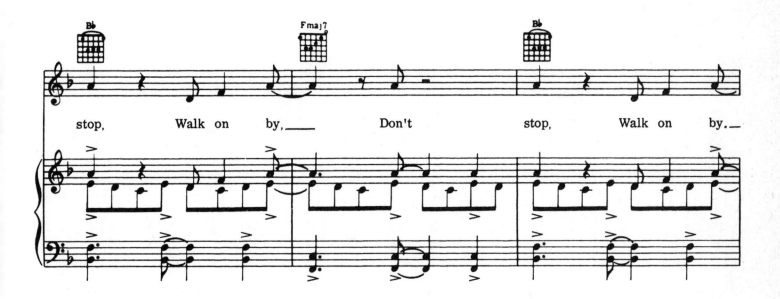

stop, Walk on by,___ Don't stop, Walk on by.___

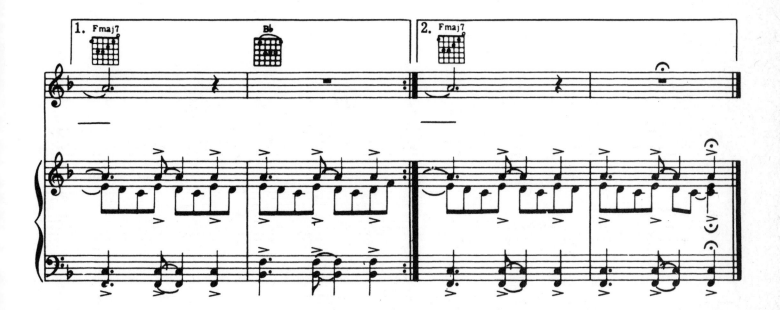

What The World Needs Now.

Music by Burt Bacharach.
Words by Hal David.

With A Jazz Waltz Feel

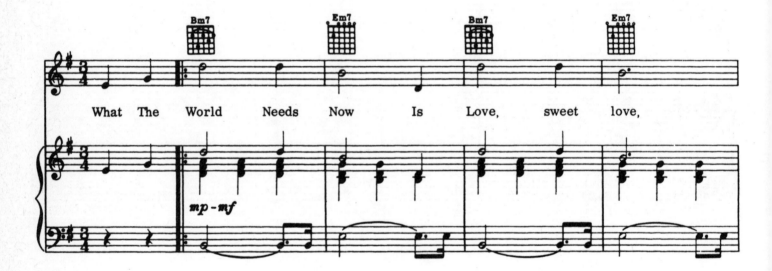

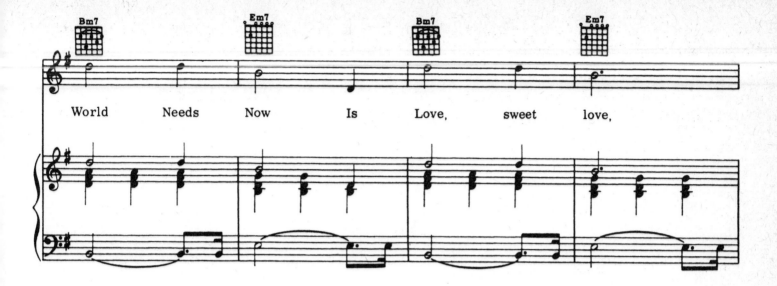

World   Needs   Now   Is   Love,   sweet   love,

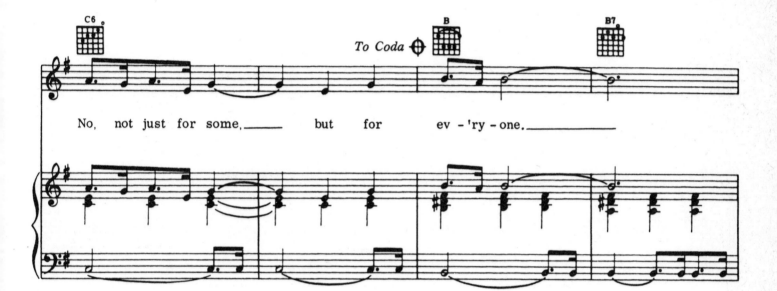

To Coda ⊕

No,   not just for some,_____ but for   ev -'ry - one._____

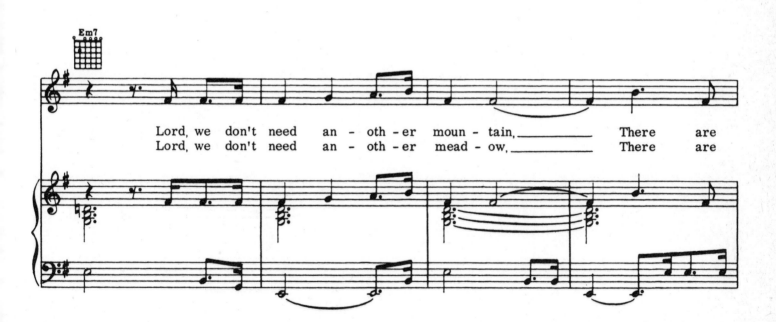

Lord,   we   don't   need   an - oth - er   moun - tain,_____ There   are
Lord,   we   don't   need   an - oth - er   mead - ow,_____ There   are

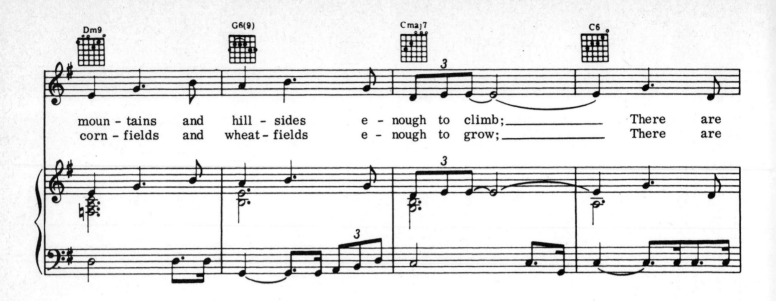

moun - tains and hill - sides e - nough to climb; ___ There are
corn - fields and wheat - fields e - nough to grow; ___ There are

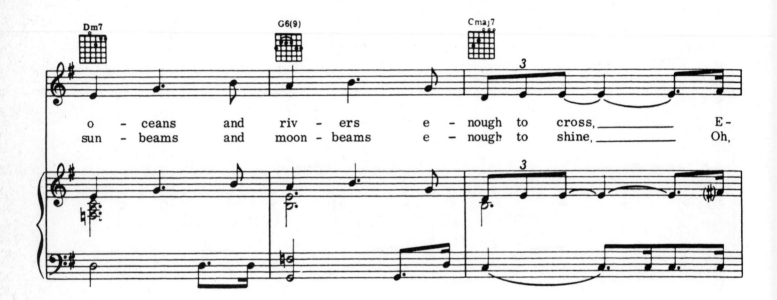

o - ceans and riv - ers e - nough to cross, ___ E-
sun - beams and moon - beams e - nough to shine, ___ Oh,

nough to last ___ till the end of time. ___ What The
lis - ten, Lord, ___ if you want to know. ___ What The

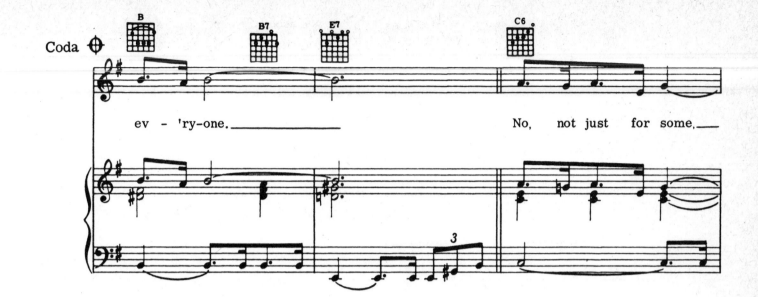

Coda

ev - 'ry-one._____ No, not just for some,____

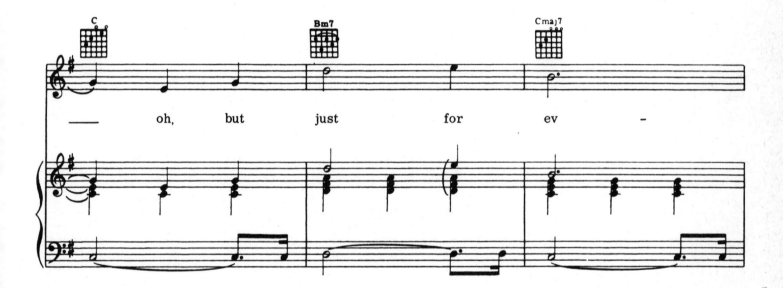

____ oh, but just for ev -

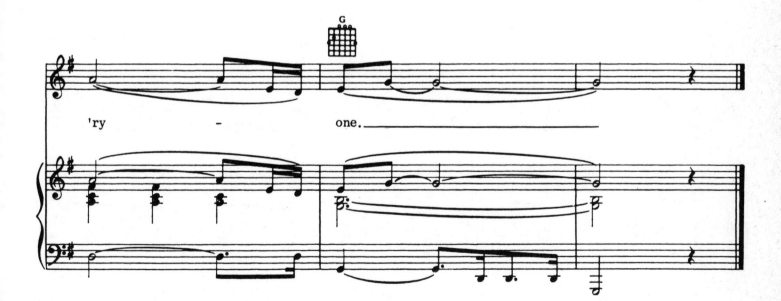

'ry - one._____

When I'm Sixty Four.

Words and music by John Lennon and Paul McCartney.

Medium tempo

When I get old - er los - ing my hair __
I could be hand - y mend-ing a fuse __
Send me a post - card, drop me a line __

ma - ny __ years from now, __ Will you still be send-ing me a
when your __ lights have gone, __ You can knit a swea-ter by the
stat-ing __ point of view, __ In - di - cate pre - cise-ly what you

Va - len - tine,— birth - day greet - ings, bot-tle of wine.—
fire - side,— Sun - day morn - ings, go for a ride.—
mean to say, — yours sin - cere - ly wast-ing a - way. —

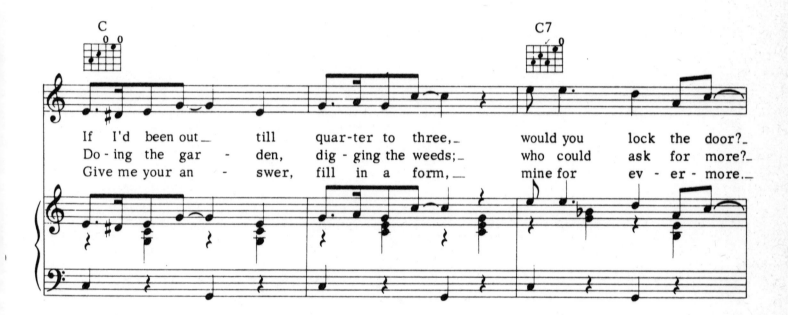

If I'd been out— till quar-ter to three,— would you lock the door?—
Do - ing the gar - den, dig - ging the weeds;— who could ask for more?—
Give me your an - swer, fill in a form, — mine for ev - er - more.—

Will you still need— me, will you still feed — me when I'm six-ty -

four?

[tacet 1st time]

[1st] Oo _____

[2nd] Ev-'ry sum-mer we can rent a cot-tage in the Isle of Wight,_

_____

___ if it's not too dear. ___

You'll be old - er

[ah]_____

We shall scrimp and

[We shall scrimp and

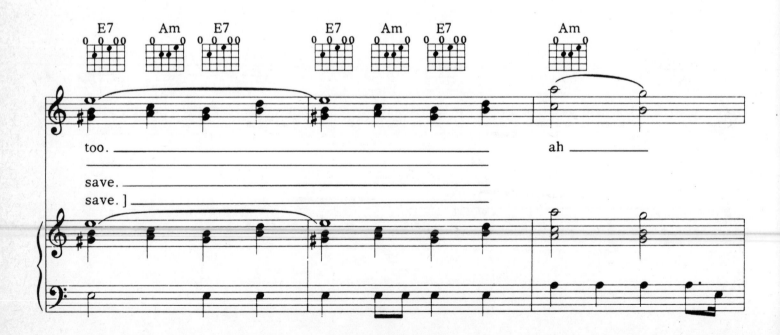

too. _____

ah _____

save. _____

save.] _____

And if you say the word_____ I could
Grand - chil - dren on your knee,_____ Ve - ra,

stay with you.
Chuck and Dave.

four? [Ho!]

What Now My Love.

Music by G. Becaud, English lyric by Carl Sigman.
Original French lyric by P. Delanoe.

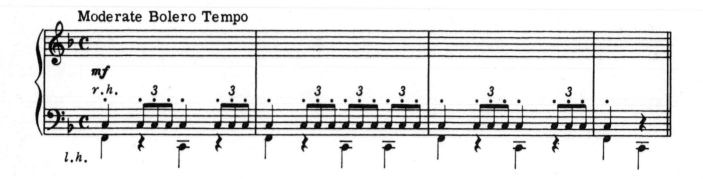

What Now My Love _____ Now that you left me _____ How can I
Love _____ Now that it's o - ver _____ I feel the

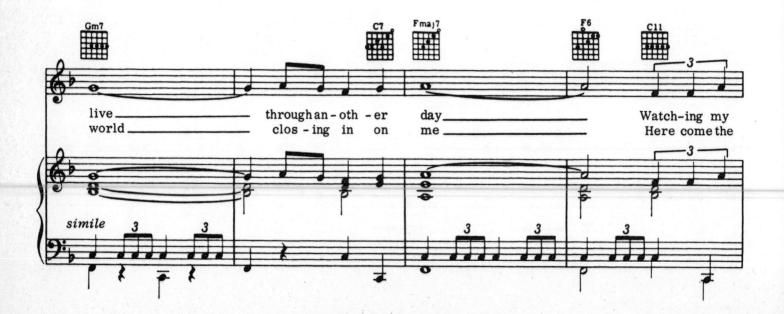

live _____ through an - oth - er day _____ Watch-ing my
world _____ clos - ing in on me _____ Here come the

dreams _____ Turn - ing to ash - es _____ And my
stars _____ Tum - bling a - round me _____ There's the

hopes _____ in - to bits of clay _____ Once I could
sky _____ where the sea should be _____ What Now My

see _____ Once I could feel _____ Now I am
Love _____ Now that you're gone _____ I'd be a

269

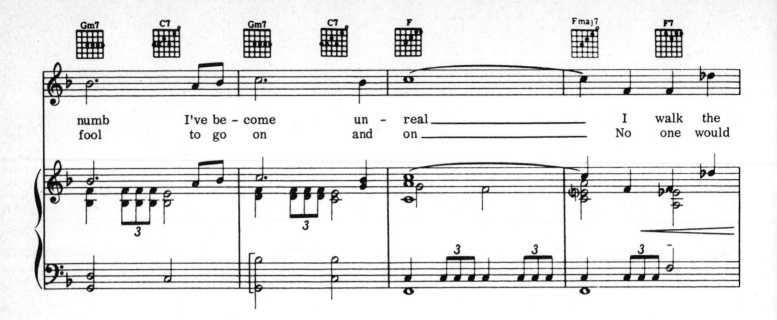

numb   I've be - come   un - real _____   I walk the
fool   to go on   and on _____   No one would

night _____ With - out a goal _____ Stripped of my
care _____ No one would cry _____ If I should

heart, _____ my soul. _____ What Now My
live _____ or die. _____

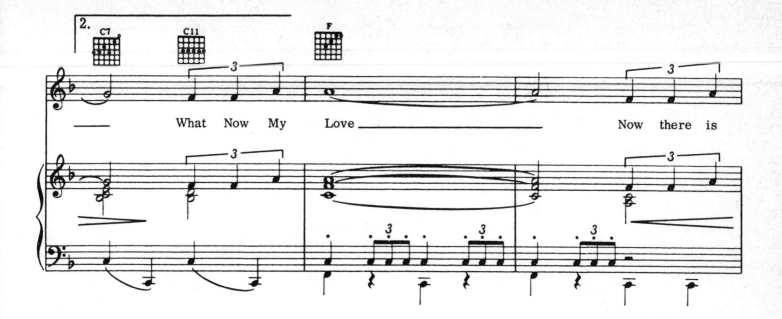

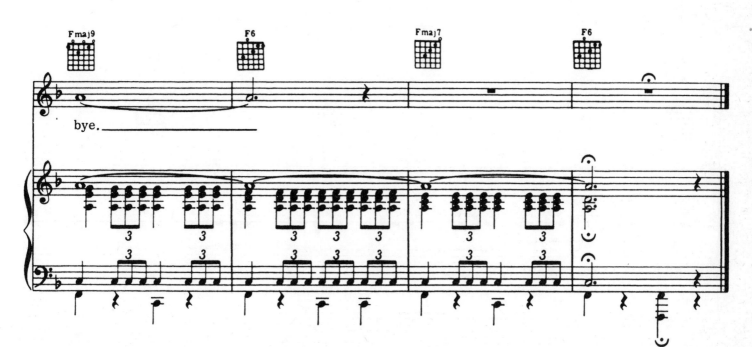

Where Have All The Flowers Gone?

Words and music by Peter Seeger.

Moderately slow, with simplicity

1. Where Have All The Flow-ers Gone? Long time pass-ing.
2. Where have all the young girls gone? Long time pass-ing.
3. Where have all the young men gone? Long time pass-ing.

Where Have All The Flow-ers Gone? Long time a-go.
Where have all the young girls gone? Long time a-go.
Where have all the young men gone? Long time a-go.

Where Have All The Flow-ers Gone? The girls have picked them ev-'ry one.
Where have all the young girls gone? They've tak-en hus-bands ev-'ry one.
Where have all the young men gone? They're all in u-ni-form.

Oh, when will they ev-er learn? Oh, when will they ev-er
Oh, when will they ev-er learn? Oh, when will they ev-er
Oh, when will they ev-er learn? Oh, when will they ev-er

1. 2.
learn?
learn?

3.
learn?

rit.

p

4. Where have all the soldiers gone? Long time passing.
   Where have all the soldiers gone? Long time ago.
   Where have all the soldiers gone?
   They've gone to graveyards, every one.
   Oh, when will they ever learn?
   Oh, when will they ever learn?

5. Where have all the graveyards gone? Long time passing.
   Where have all the graveyards gone? Long time ago.
   Where have all the graveyards gone?
   They're covered with flowers, every one.
   Oh, when will they ever learn?
   Oh, when will they ever learn?

6. Where Have All The Flowers Gone? Long time passing.
   Where Have All The Flowers Gone? Long time ago.
   Where Have All The Flowers Gone?
   Young girls picked them, every one.
   Oh, when will they ever learn?
   Oh, when will they ever learn?

We Shall Overcome.

New words and music adaptation by Zilphia Horton, Frank Hamilton, Guy Carawan and Pete Seeger.

Moderately slow with determination

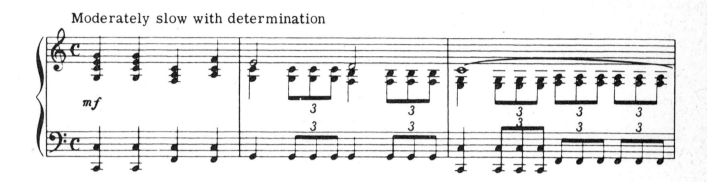

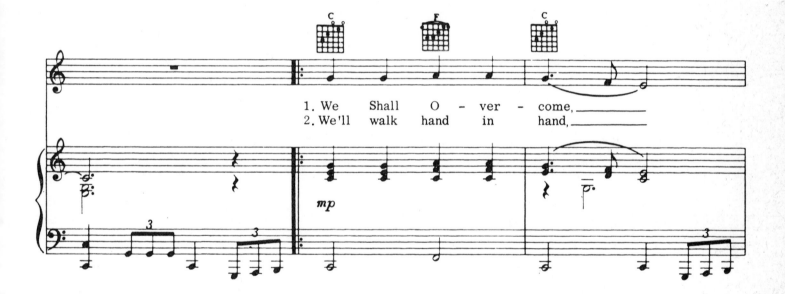

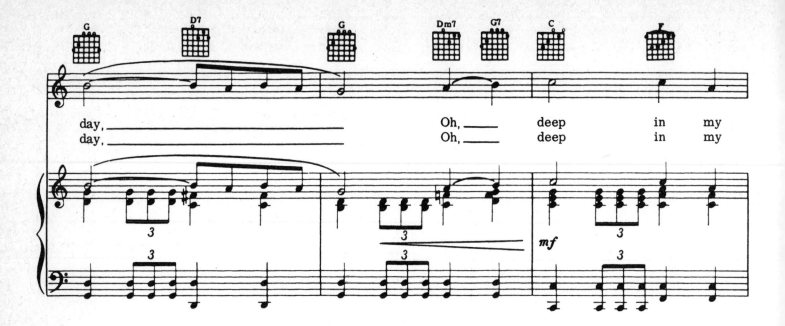

day, _____ Oh, _____ deep in my
day, _____ Oh, _____ deep in my

heart   I   do   be – lieve
heart   I   do   be – lieve

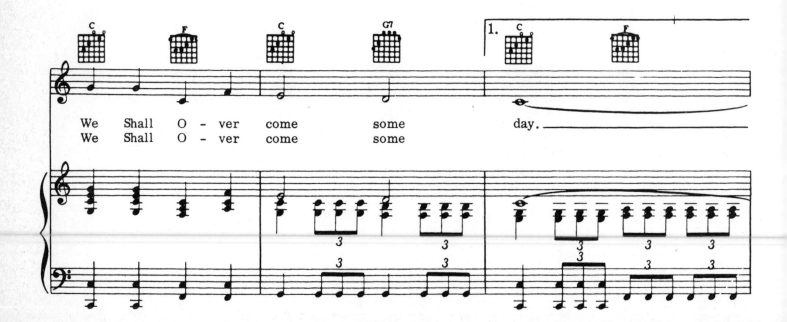

We Shall O – ver come   some   day. _____
We Shall O – ver come   some

276

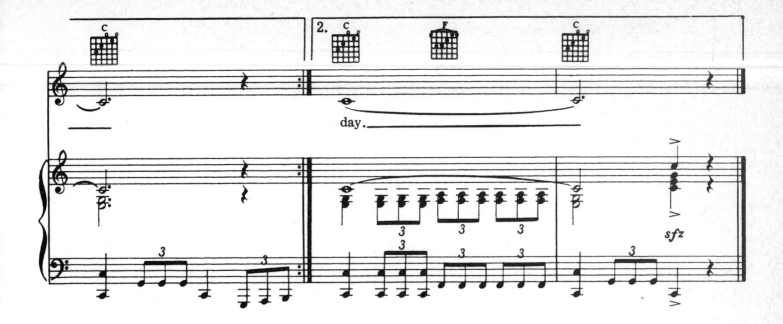

day.

3. We are not afraid, we are not afraid,
   We are not afraid today,
   Oh, deep in my heart I do believe
   We shall overcome some day.

4. We shall stand together, we shall stand together,
   We shall stand together – now,
   Oh, deep in my heart I do believe
   We shall overcome some day.

5. The truth will make us free, the truth will make us free,
   The truth will make us free some day,
   Oh, deep in my heart I do believe
   We shall overcome some day.

6. The Lord will see us through, the Lord will see us through,
   The Lord will see us through some day,
   Oh, deep in my heart I do believe
   We shall overcome some day.

7. We shall be like Him, we shall be like Him,
   We shall be like Him someday,
   Oh, deep in my heart I do believe
   We shall overcome someday.

8. We shall live in peace, we shall live in peace,
   We shall live in peace some day,
   Oh, deep in my heart I do believe
   We shall overcome some day.

9. The whole wide world around, the whole wide world around,
   The whole wide world around some day,
   Oh, deep in my heart I do believe
   We shall overcome some day.

10. We shall overcome, we shall overcome,
    We shall overcome some day,
    Oh, deep in my heart I do believe
    We shall overcome some day.

Winchester Cathedral.

Words and music by Geoff Stephens.

Easy tempo

Win - ches-ter Ca - the - dral   you're bring-ing me down,

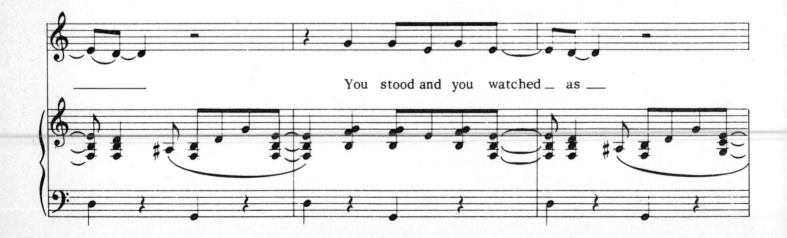

You stood and you watched as

my ba-by left town.___ You could have done some - thing,___

but you did-n't try._____ You did-n't do no-

- thing,___ you let her walk by.

Now ev-'ry-one knows ___ just how much ___ I need-ed that girl, ___

She would-n't have gone ___ far a - way ___ If on-ly you'd

start-ed ring-ing your bell. ___ Win-chester Ca-the - dral, ___

you're bring-ing me down. _____ You stood and you watched_

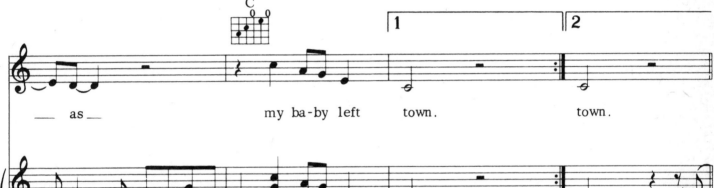

_ as _ my ba-by left town. town.

1 **2**

A Whiter Shade Of Pale.

Words and music by Keith Reid and Gary Brooker.

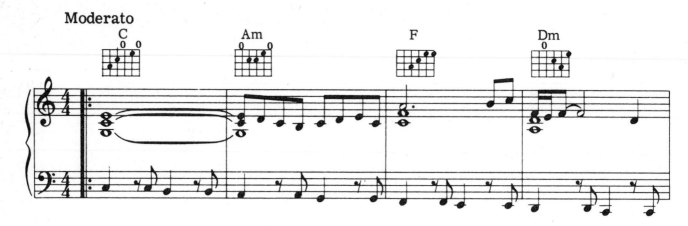

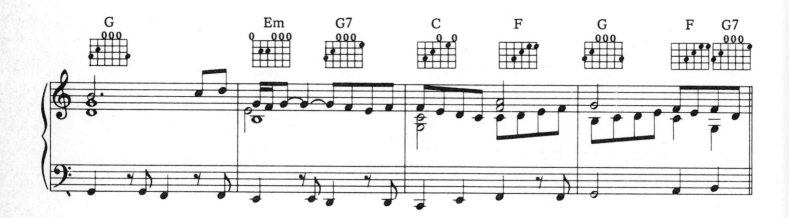

We skipped the light fan-dan-go And turned cartwheels 'cross the
She said, "There is no rea-son, And the truth is ___ plain to

floor.___
see.",___

I was feel-ing kind of sea-sick,
But I wan-dered through my play-ing cards

But the crowd called out for more,
And would not_ let her be.

The room was humming har-der
One of six-teen vest-al vir-gins

As the cei-ling flew a - way.__
Who were lea-ving for the coast,_

When we called out for a - no - ther drink
And al-tho' my eyes were o - pen

The wai-ter brought a tray,— And so it was ___ that la - ter
They might just as well been closed,

As the mil - ler told his tale,—   That her face at first just

ghostly,   Turned a whi-ter___ shade of pale.___   pale.___

The Windmills Of Your Mind.

Lyric by Marilyn and Alan Bergman.
Music by Michel Legrand.

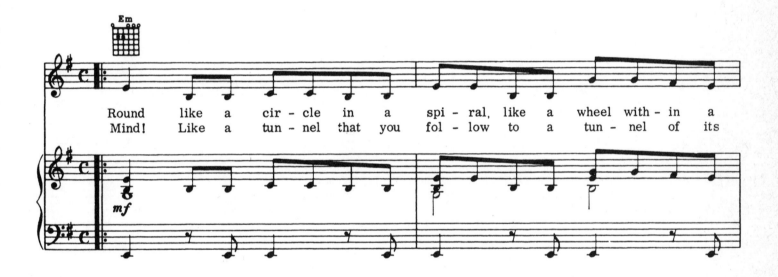

Round like a cir-cle in a spi-ral, like a wheel with-in a
Mind! Like a tun-nel that you fol-low to a tun-nel of its

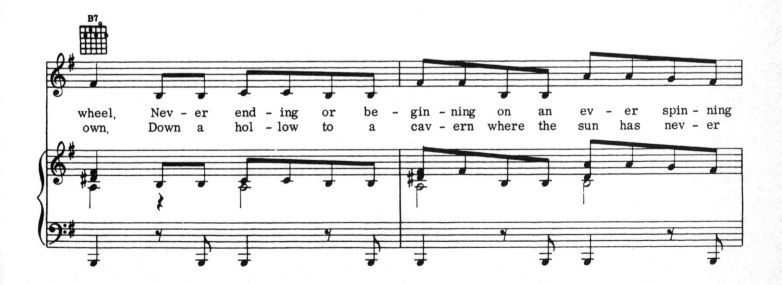

wheel, Nev-er end-ing or be-gin-ning on an ev-er spin-ning
own, Down a hol-low to a cav-ern where the sun has nev-er

sand. Is the sound of dis - tant drum-ming just the fin - gers of your

hand? Pic - tures hang - ing in a hall - way and the frag - ment of a

song, Half re - mem-bered names and fac - es, but to whom do they be -

long? When you knew that it was o - ver you were sud - den - ly a -
(Girl) When you knew that it was o - ver in the au - tumn of good-

289

With A Little Help From My Friends.

Words and music by John Lennon and Paul McCartney.

you a song,— and I'll try — not to sing— out of key.— Oh I get by—
of the day? (are you sad — be-cause you're on your own? — No I get by—
out the light?)— I can't tell — you,but I know— it's mine. Oh I get by

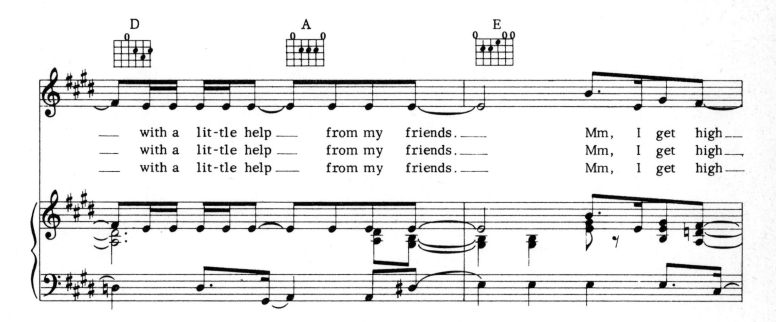

— with a lit-tle help — from my friends.— Mm, I get high—
— with a lit-tle help — from my friends.— Mm, I get high—
— with a lit-tle help — from my friends.— Mm, I get high—

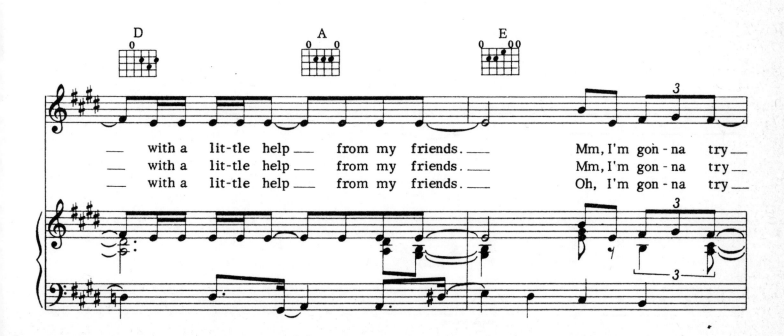

— with a lit-tle help — from my friends.— Mm, I'm gon-na try—
— with a lit-tle help — from my friends.— Mm, I'm gon-na try—
— with a lit-tle help — from my friends.— Oh, I'm gon-na try—

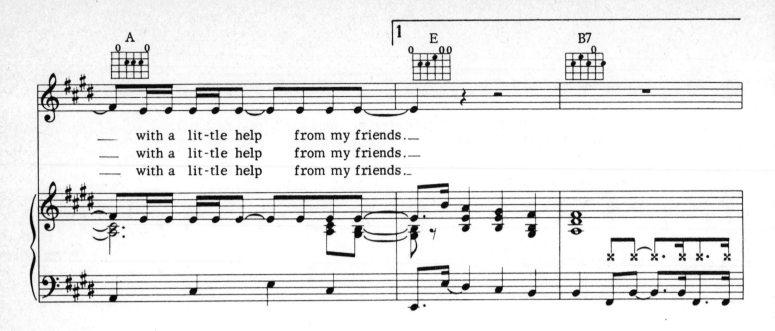

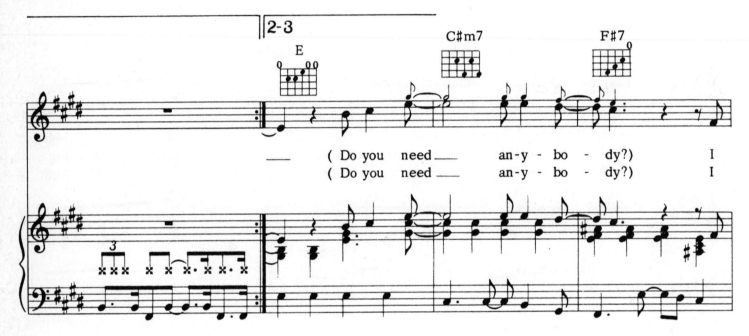

- dy?) I want some - bo - dy to love.___
- dy?) I want some - bo - dy to love.__

D.S. al ⊕ 𝄌

⊕ *Coda*

___ Oh, I get by ___ with a lit - tle help ___ from my friends.__

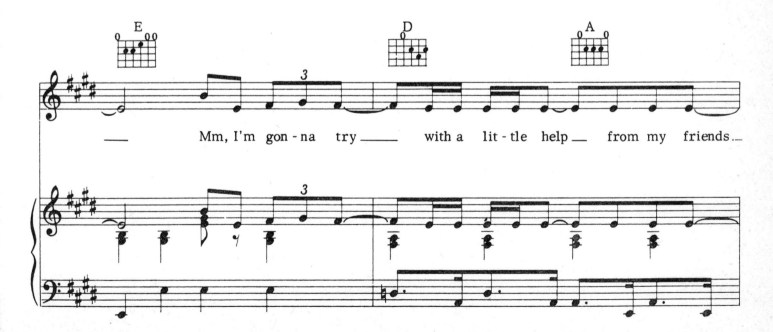

___ Mm, I'm gon - na try ___ with a lit - tle help ___ from my friends.__

Oh, I get high___ with a lit-tle help___from my friends.___ Yes, I get by___

___ with a lit-tle help___ from my friends, with a lit-tle help___ from my friends.___

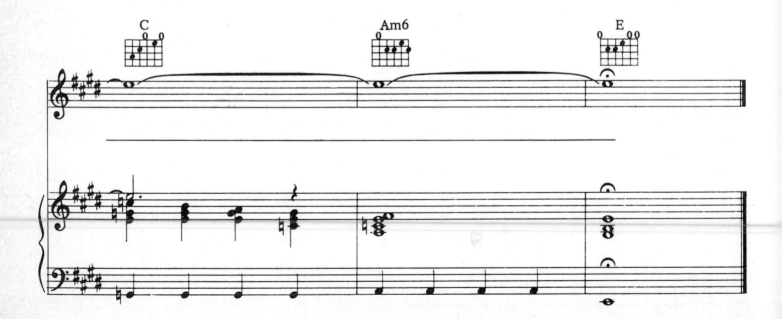

Wooden Heart.

Words and music by Fred Wise, Ben Weisman, Kay Twomey and Berthold Kaempfert.

Moderately (in 2)

Can't you see I love you, Please don't break my heart in two,

That's not hard to do, 'Cause I don't have a wood - en heart.

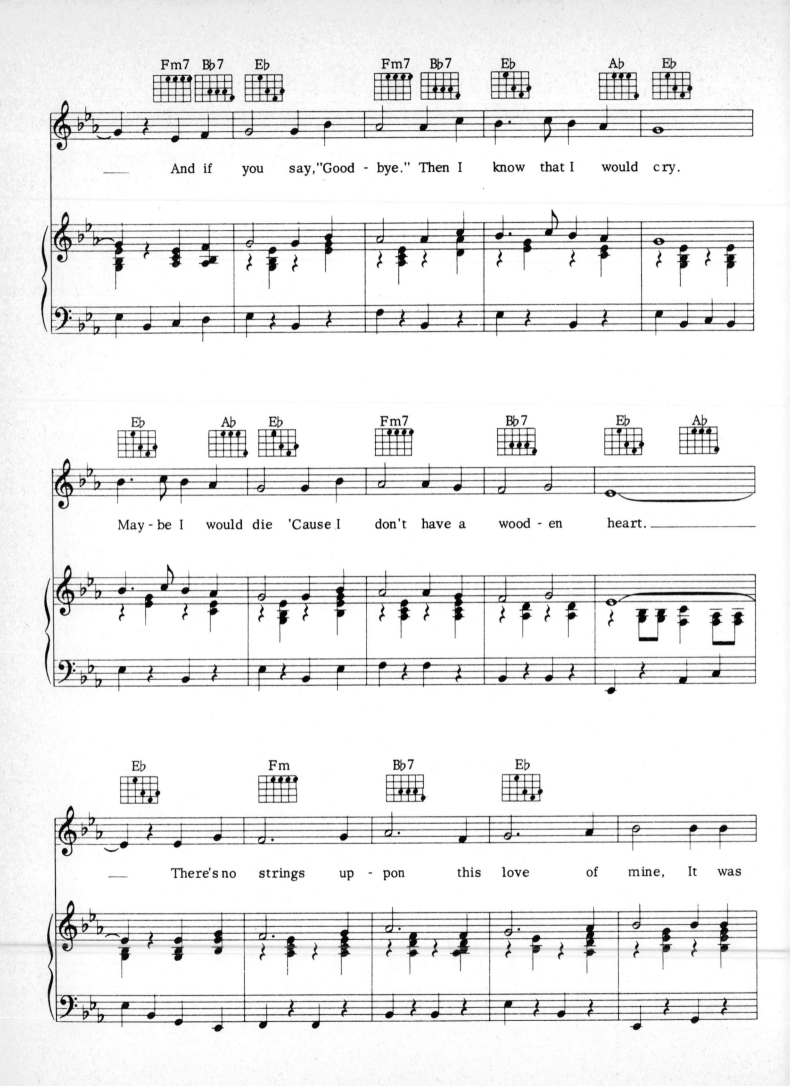

And if you say,"Good - bye." Then I know that I would cry.

May - be I would die 'Cause I don't have a wood - en heart.

There's no strings up - on this love of mine, It was

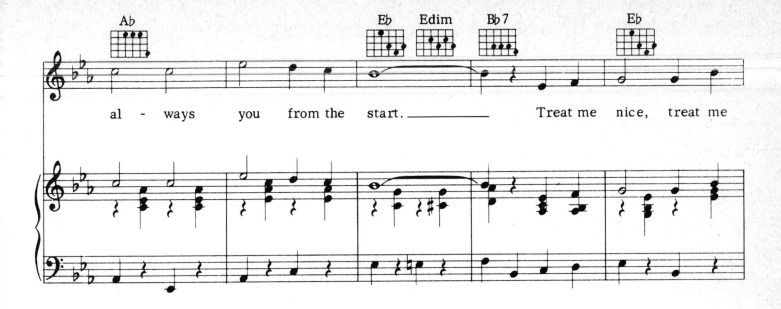

al - ways you from the start. _____ Treat me nice, treat me

good, treat me like you real - ly should, 'Cause I'm not made of

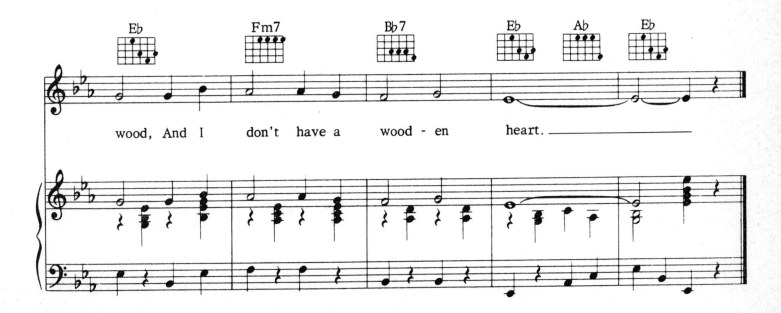

wood, And I don't have a wood - en heart. _____

Yellow Submarine.

Words and music by John Lennon and Paul McCartney.

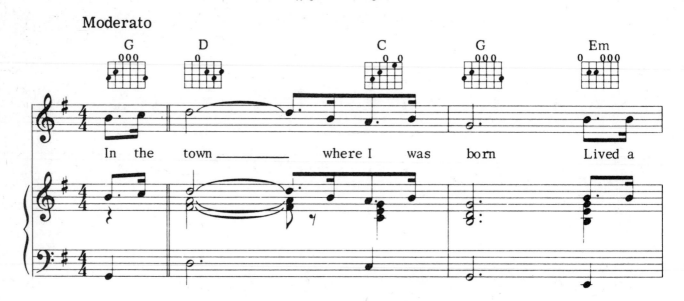

found _____ the sea of green, And we lived _____ be-neath the

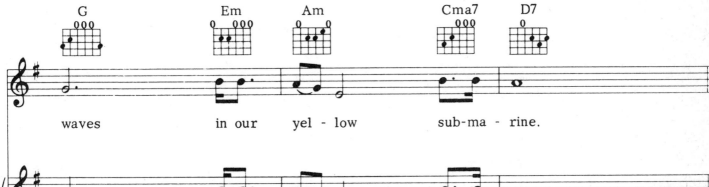

waves   in our   yel - low   sub-ma - rine.

We all live in a   yel -low sub-ma-rine,   yel-low sub-ma-rine,   yel -low sub-ma-rine.

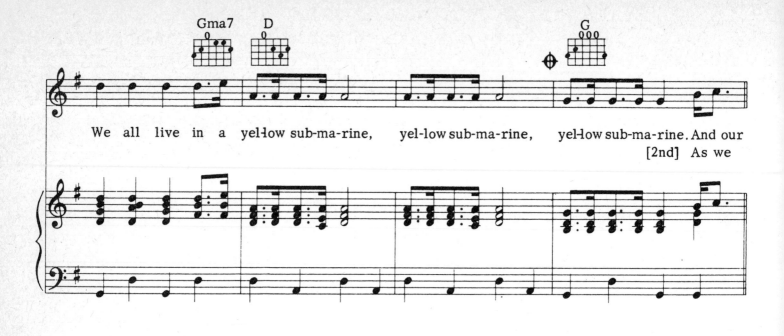

We all live in a yel-low sub-ma-rine, yel-low sub-ma-rine, yel-low sub-ma-rine. And our
[2nd] As we

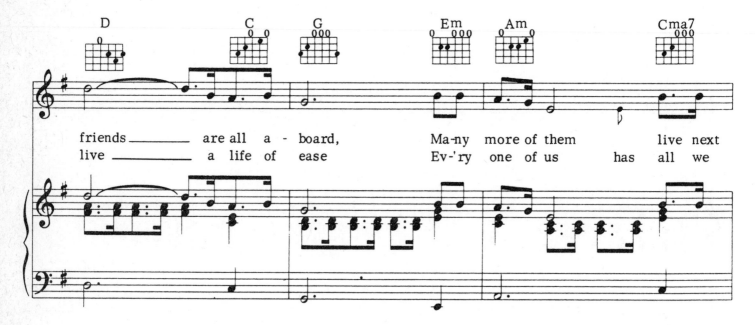

friends _____ are all a - board, Ma-ny more of them live next
live _____ a life of ease Ev-'ry one of us has all we

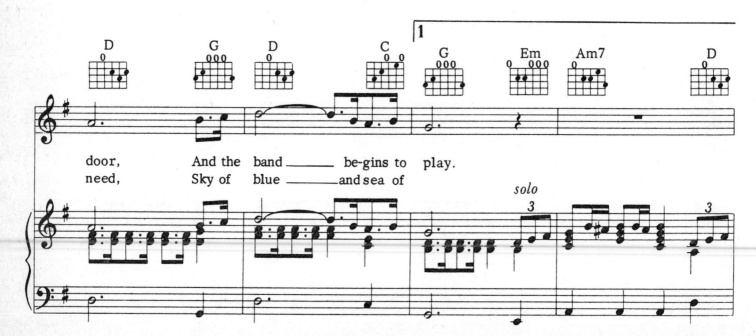

door, And the band _____ be-gins to play.
need, Sky of blue _____ and sea of

solo

green   In our yel-low   sub-ma-rine.

Coda

yel-low sub-ma-rine.   We al live in a yel-low sub-ma-rine,   yel-low sub-ma-rine,

fade 2nd time

yel-low sub-ma-rine.   We all live in a yel-low sub-ma-rine,   yel-low sub-ma-rine.

You're My World.

Original lyrics by Gino Paoli.
Music by Umberto Bindi. Words by Carl Sigman.

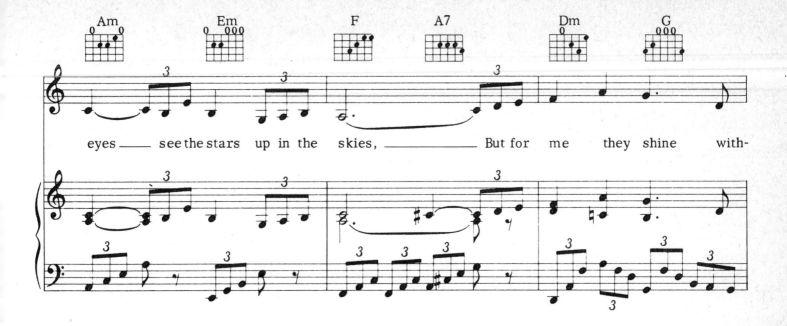

eyes —— see the stars up in the skies, ——————— But for me they shine with-

in your eyes.— As the trees reach for the sun a - bove, So my

arms reach out to you for love; With your hand rest - ing in

mine   I feel a pow - er so ___ di - vine. ___ You're my

world,   you are my night,   my   day;   You're my

world,   you're ev-'ry pray'r I   pray.   If our

love   cea-ses to be   Then it's the   end of my world___ for

me._____   You're my   end of my world,   end of my world,

end _____ of my   world   for   me._____

Yesterday.

Words and music by John Lennon and Paul McCartney.

Moderately

p e dolce

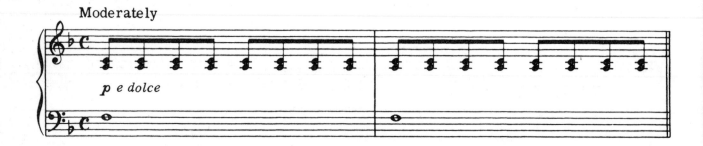

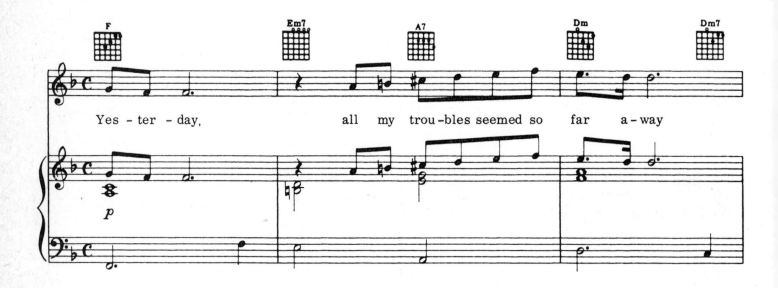

Yes - ter - day, all my trou - bles seemed so far a - way

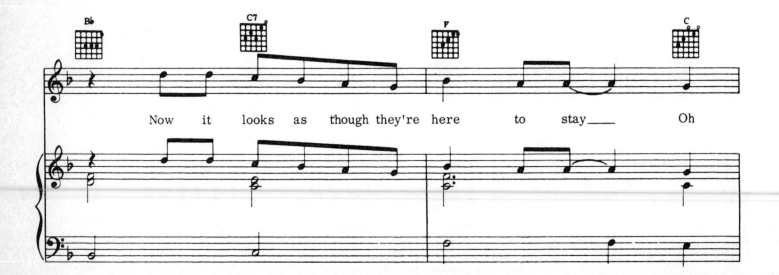

Now it looks as though they're here to stay___ Oh

I be - lieve___ in yes - ter - day.___ Sud - den - ly

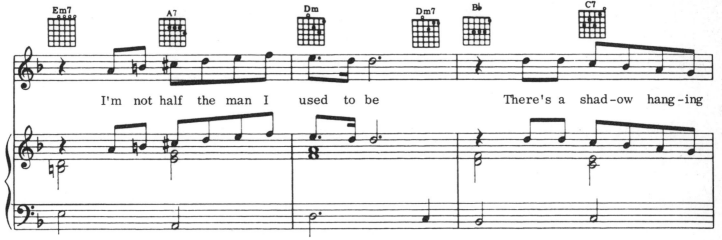

I'm not half the man I used to be There's a shad - ow hang - ing

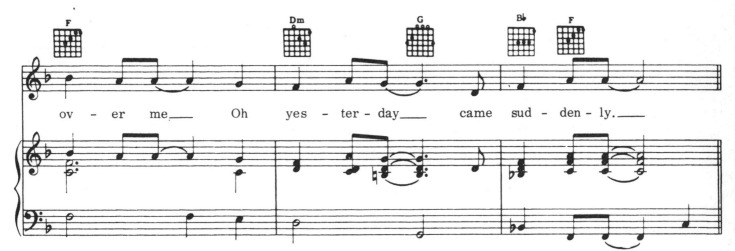

ov - er me___ Oh yes - ter - day___ came sud - den - ly.___

Why she had to go I don't know, she would - n't say.

I said some-thing wrong now I long for yes-ter-day.

Yes-ter-day, love was such an eas-y game to play

Now I need a place to hide a-way___ Oh I be-lieve___ in

yes-ter-day.___ Mm mm mm mm mm.___